TRAVELS IN THE DRIFTING DAWN

To Marie-Claude
for all kinds of reasons

TRAVELS IN THE DRIFTING DAWN

KENNETH WHITE

MAINSTREAM
PUBLISHING

The Publisher acknowledges subsidy of the Scottish Arts
Council in the production of this volume.

Copyright © Kenneth White, 1989
All rights reserved
First published in Great Britain in 1989 by
MAINSTREAM PUBLISHING COMPANY (EDINBURGH) LTD
7 Albany Street
Edinburgh EH1 3UG
ISBN 1 85158 2401 (cloth)

British Library Cataloguing in Publication Data

White, Kenneth
   Travels in the drifting dawn
   I. Title
   823'.914 [F]

ISBN 1-85158-240-1

Typeset by C. R. Barber & Partners (Highlands) Ltd
Fort William, Scotland
Printed in Great Britain by Billings & Sons Ltd, Worcester

CONTENTS

He who leaves the world without having seen his real place has not fully lived.

Brihadaranyaka Upanishad

I've walked and wandered, slept on a hundred islands, knocked about in a hundred towns.

Taliesin

Drifting, drifting—what am I more than a lone gull between earth and sky?

Tu Fu

PREFACE

I

Drifting, drifting . . . that's the way it looks on the edges of our civilisation. A drifting, a searching, beyond all the known grounds, for an *other* ground.

It's this *other* ground that is the theme of the heregathered texts—an other ground: a space of being, an area of the mind; and the way(s) to it. So that the book is a book of travelling, the account of a displacement going deeper than geography, by someone who is first and foremost a pedestrian, sometimes a hitch-hiker, always a precarious inhabitant, just passing through.

Europe at one time knew a species of wandering monks, quiet, but determined—they went by the name of Key, Maklou, Kolomban—whose traces can be found from Galway to Prague and from Cologne to Madrid, and who brought a moving brightness to its sky.

The drifter of this book often thought of them, and their like on other continents, but there is nothing religious about him (except maybe in a special a-theistic sense), and his mysticism, if mysticism there is, is strongly tinged with a laughing *gai savoir*. Again, if he may seem to have retained some archaic connections, he is essentially the modern man: 'standing before a void, out of which all things may grow.'

2

To speak now more precisely of literature.

Given the radical situation outlined above, and the sense of identity I live with, I've found it useful to work at and work out three types of book: poem-books, prose-books and essay-books, each type influencing the other. At one point, I likened this triple literary activity to an arrow. The essays, maintaining direction, are the feathers; the prose, ongoing autobiography, or what I like to call 'way-books' (alias transcendental travelogues) is the arrow's shaft; and the poem is the arrow-head. And of course the whole arrow is in movement, going somewhere, not just marking time or making remarks about this, that and the next thing.

Which is to say in passing (I don't want to waste time in polemic) that I've been trying, as writer, to get out of the present rather dreary, and deadening, compartmentalisation of 'novel', 'verse', 'philosophy'. Poetry and philosophy I take to be fast, clear, grounded sensation and thinking. As to 'telling the story', the novel, essentially a time-form, took over from myth, which is tied to origin. It's when myth is still there, as in *Moby Dick*, or when the body-mind grapples directly with time, as in Proust, that it still remains primal and has strength. But the novel's been running down for some time now, and what seems to me to mark the twentieth century is not so much time as space (think of Joyce's attempt to get out of the nightmare of history). We're looking for a new space-art, a new spatial movement, which means new mindscape. That, fundamentally, is what *Travels in the Drifting Dawn*, initiating my outward movement, is all about.

3

The first texts grew from the years 1963 to 1966, when, having come back from four years' expatriation in Paris, I was at once uproariously active and hilariously desperate in Britain's all too insulated culture-context (I was on my own, but had lateral connections with Project Sigma). These texts go from London underground to Celtic shore, passing through various towns and cities, mainly Edinburgh and Glasgow, the intellectual and the cosmogonical. Thereafter comes a break, and we're back on the Continent, where the wanderings continue, from Amsterdam in the north to Barcelona in the south, with a loop over again to Scotland (the movement is complex!) and a little aside to North Africa. During all this time, and throughout these excursions, Paris is still the principal centre (later, there would be *no* centre), but is not mentioned here. The Paris notebooks, the core as it were of this choreography, constitute another volume, *Incandescent Limbo*, of which, perhaps ('au revoir, Meester Martin') more later.

K.W.

PART I

THE SOLITUDES

As he travels through the great human desert, this man, this lonely figure endowed with active imagination, has, you may be sure, a higher aim, a more general aim, than that of a mere strolling reporter.

Baudelaire

UNDERGROUND LONDON

*. . . it is not the underground that is better, but
something different, quite different, for which I
am thirsting, but which I cannot find. Damn the
underground!*

Dostoyevsky

I

When I phoned that morning from the floozy precincts of
Victoria, I was invited to come right over, and soon found
myself before the decaying yellow façade of the house in
Bayswater where my co-abolitionist and resurrectionist Joe
Torelli, late of Glasgow, New York and Chihuahua, had made
his temporary abode, open to all vagrants, poets and undefined
individuals.

It was friend Joe himself came to the door—long and thin,
beak-nosed, with a purple-stoned necklace round his neck and a
crimson fez on his head—and ushered me volubly into the
kitchen where sat Luke, one of Joe's followers, wondering aloud
what to do with the seven pounds of hot pot which a girl-friend
of his had brought over with her from Mexico in the innocent
guts of a teddy-bear. Since this had been the subject of
conversation before I turned up, and since it was pressing, it
was now resumed.

'Now look here, Luke, we just can't have all that stuff lying
around here like it was liquorice allsorts or something. I mean
it's crazy, man, *crazy*. You can get fifteen years for that, you
understand? You don't want that, do you? More important, *I*
don't want it.'

'OK, man, lay off.'

'And don't think you're going to be able to just get out there and sell it on the streets. This is a *civilized* country. Pot is *strictly not allowed.*'

'I know, man.'

'Well, now you *know*, you better start *thinking* some. The sooner that stuff's out of this house, the easier I'll feel. I mean seven whole pounds, it's *crazy*.' He turned to me: 'This cat's dangerous to have around,' he said.

Luke grinned:

'Let's have some cawffee.'

2

In the year of our Lord, 1614, in Cassel, Germany, the world of alchemists, Paracelsians, Theosophists, etc., was startled by the publication of pamphlets bearing the title: The Fame of the Fraternity of the Meritorious Order of the Rosy Cross. *These were the proclamations of certain anonymous men who claimed to have achieved a synthesis of all the sciences and to possess the true and occult truth concerning the universe. 'Europe is with child,' they cried, and kept on publishing inflammatory pamphlets by the score.*

(Introduction to the Portfolio)

3

'Man, it is happening,' said Joe, 'and when it really gets under way, why nothing's going to stop it, nothing.'

'That's for sure,' said Luke.

'You must give our friend the whole Portfolio with all the plans,' said Joe, 'so he can get boned up on all the various aspects of our activities. These islands have seen nothing like it since Boadicea put on her blue paint and went on the war-path.'

'Damn right,' said Luke.

Joe went over to a table littered with paintings and bits of sculpture, took a syringe from a blue egg-cup and, sticking it into his left arm, pressed the bulb, replaced the syringe in the blue egg-cup, and continued:

'We're negotiating at the moment with a wireless station outside the three-mile limit which we intend to use, and I mean *use*, for propaganda purposes.'

'Radio revolution,' said Luke.

'Then,' said Joe, 'I've just been invited to Cuba by Fidel Castro to give talks on psychedelic sculpture to revolutionary students. Not that I want to get mixed up with the Cuban caper. Communism's strictly for the dodos, like everything else. But we can use the opportunity.'

'Yeah,' said Luke.

Suddenly there was a commotion in the street outside.

'Ssssh,' said Joe, with upraised, silencing finger, then, with shoulders hunched and on tip-toe, he slipped into the hall-way and stood there listening, like something out of the Arabian Nights. Luke and I came up behind him.

'Are they in?' said a voice.

'Try the door.'

'Knock it bloody well down.'

Squaring his shoulders, Joe went heroically to the door and opened it.

Three workmen, trying to manoeuvre a length of lead piping, grinned cockneyly up at him. Joe grinned back:

'It's this lead pipe,' one said.

'OK,' said Joe, and held the door open while they completed their manoeuvre. Then he closed the door, thoughtful.

'Here,' he said, 'get that damned pot. I don't want to be scared like that again,' pulling a table from the wall and revealing hollow spaces in its frame.

Luke came back with three brown-paper packets. The two of them began stuffing the pot-packets into the space.

Then we went back into the kitchen, and Joe began to expose his shit-hot ideas concerning psychedelic toilet paper.

4

In 1957, or thereabouts, at the Star Observatory, Green Bank, West Virginia, USA, a project (Project Ozma) was set in motion with the aim of seeking out life on other planets. This will entail a systematic survey of all likely stars in the neighbourhood of the sun, the most likely being those of the K group.

(Introduction to the Portfolio)

5

Next morning, we're rolling through the streets of London in a taxi driven by Luke, having collected from their hotel Paul, a jazzman, and Heinrich, a poet who had just published a new series of *Utopian Upanishads* in San Francisco and who, with a trip to Nepal behind him, was to be working with Joe on a book called *High on Hasheesh*.

'If you feel your bottom's hot,' said Joe, 'it's because of what's under the seat.' The pot had changed its hiding place.

'Does Luke always buy taxis?' asked Heinrich.

'Yes, it's handier for our purposes,' said Joe, 'we preserve a certain, mmm, anonymity that way.'

When we arrive at the house in Bayswater, we meet Joe's loving wife on the stairs.

'Is lunch ready, lover?' says Joe.

'No,' says his wife, like to a jerk.

'Any food in the house?' says Joe.

'No,' says his wife, and moves, indifferently and stolidly, off.

'You bitch,' says Joe, then, 'I think all of us mother-fuckers had better go round to the joint on the corner.'

So we go round to the joint on the corner which is Bill's Cosy Café, one of Britain's best, and when the waitress has come up and is nonchalantly slopping up the stew-juice on our table, she asks what we want, and Joe asks if she has any corned beef:

'Like, not out of tins,' he says.

'All corned beef's out of tins,' she says.

'No,' says Joe, 'all corned beef is *not* out of tins, but if all you have is corned beef out of *tins*, then give me some *eggs*, unless they also come out of tins.'

'You can have eggs out of hens,' said the waitress, who was a pretty smart cookie after all, and took the other orders for stew and cheese and beans.

6

'Tonight at ten. Meeting of the friends of Mt Shasta and other arctic explorers. Bring your own stuff.'

7

And His kingdom shall be established in your lifetimes and your days, and the lifetimes of all Israel. Orion, the nebula of Orion, like the proto-ghost of a giant purple bird. The Crab, a great luminous brain in space. Under the ribs. In the veins. Back to root sources. What dada did. Eternal eros. The old calligrapher who loved geese. The original face. Chaos and creation, alienation and creativity. A Mexico of the mind. European euphoria. A no, a yes, a straight line, a goal. Cats and catharsis. Mister Charlie Parker. The big secession. A new anthropology. The hyperborean wild swans. The Amber Road. No Thule the ultimate one. *Brumosa extrema ultima.* Dreamers, mystics, and intellectuals. Explosive incandescences, tormented irradiations. Black, ochrous, sulphurous, purple, copper-yellow. The great waterfalls of the Gullfoss. Curiosities of erotic physiology. Sex and revolution. Work the dumb oracle. Twat! Joyce—the sick catholic; Lawrence—the hysterical puritan; Miller—the obscene mystic. Artaud, Daumal, Bataille. Saints and prophets. Ariane and Dionysus. How to connect with the social-political men. The Ishmaelites, cunt-worshippers. Red totem among the trees.

Wakinyan! Wakonda! Ketchimanetowa! Buffalo-girl dressed in white leather. Lone Man born from a red flower. The platonic education of desire. Psyche receives wings from eros. The place and the formula. Significant space. Hegel—'thinking is essentially the negation of what is immediately before us.' The emergence of new modes of existence with new forms of reason and freedom. Psycho-experimental speculation. Hemp used as a de-inhibiting factor in tantric practices. The basic sakt coiled up in the base-centre of the yogic body. Numinogenic. Enstasy and ecstasy. Shiva the lord of herbs. Oneiric delirium. Paranoid use of language. Lingo-lingam. Consciousness overflowing beyond the limit. Take in more of the complexities and possibilities of the real world. Ecstatic materialism. Imaginative energy. An aberration from the point of view of practical utility. Break-away from merely adaptive behaviour. The red and dark-brown arkoses of Applecross. Blue boulder clay crossed by gneiss. Up in the barren red. Hindu girl with a blue muslin sari. Provide the word 'art' with a new content. 'The white of a clarity beyond the facts.' In the Tarahumara mountains. 'Let every body become a dancer and every spirit a bird.' Not either-or, but and . . . .

8

'The strange mad Satyrs are twisted and contorted to make exquisite patterns, they clash their frenzied crotala and wave great vine branches. But in the midst of the revel the god himself stands erect. He holds no kantharos, only a great lyre. His head is thrown back in ecstasy; he is drunken, but with music, not with wine.'

(Harrison: *Prolegomena to the Study of Greek Religion*)

9

I'm sitting next morning in a Lyons tearoom on Tottenham Court Road, whiling away the time before boarding the Royal

Scot, when I meet the tractor. Not a Massey-Harris, or a
Fergusson. A human tractor. Who introduced himself as a
diabetic . . ..

I'm sitting there quietly and absorbedly, having eaten a spicy
London bun gizzered and stuffed with oozy yellow butter, and
half regretting it, when a voice speaks unto me, saying:

'Enyseea?'

I look up, uncomprehendingly. Then, suddenly catching on,
I say:

'No,'

and the man sits down. It's the tractor. He has a slopping cup
of coffee with him and a bag full of—

'Fojemro,' he says.

'What's that?' I say.

'Fojemroevimoin,' he says. I take time to work it out.
Fortunately, I've had some training in linguistics. Bringing the
sounds into relation with the situation, I get his message.

'Yes, four jam rolls every morning,' he says. 'Got to. I'm a
diabetic.' Then:

'What part of the country do you come from?' he adds.

'North,' I say. 'Scotland.'

'Thought you was a foreigner,' he says.

'It took me a while to catch on to you,' I say.

'God a gumboil,' he says, pointing to his right jaw with a
jam roll. 'Gives me gyp. Have a look,' he says, and opens his
gub wide. I appreciate.

'Must be a bother eating these doughnuts every morning,' I
say.

'No,' he says. 'Enjoy id. God plenty of dime. Oud of work . . .'

'What's the badge?' I say, wanting to be friendly, pointing to
a little green-and-gold badge in his lapel.

'Scripture Union,' he says, and then in one long screed and in
a flat monotonous voice, gulping air between each section, he
reels off:

'Man shall not live by bread alone but by every word that

proceedeth out of the mouth of God. Matthew four, verse four—Thy word is a lamp unto my feet and a light unto my path. Psalm 119, verse 105—Every house is builded by some man but he that built all things is God. Hebrews three, verse four . . .'

'Where'd you get all that?' I say.

'I'm a tractor,' he says, and putting his hand in his waistcoat pocket he brings out, between index and thumb, a diminutive red-bound book.

'Littlest Bible in the world,' he says. 'Here, you can have it.'

'Thanks,' I say.

'Personal Bible. Read a verse of that every day and no harm'll come to you.'

'Thanks,' I say.

'Here, I'll sign it,' says the tractor, and takes out his pen. I slide the book over the table. On the first page of the book of the Little Bible Ministry, the tractor writes: Albert Henry Morris.

'That's very kind of you,' I say.

'I sell them 2d to them I think as can afford it,' he says, 'but you can have that one free.'

'Thanks a lot.'

'Thou shalt love thy neighbour as thyself,' says Albert. 'Good luck to you, Jock.'

'Good luck to you, Albert.'

10

'*I've heard that, in England, a fish broke surface and uttered a couple of words in such an outlandish language that scholars have been trying to work out their meaning for three years—so far in vain.*'

(Gogol's madman)

11

At three o'clock that afternoon, after five hours watching the landscape, I take a seat in the dining car opposite a middle-aged

Englishwoman who is studying the tea menu. She doesn't half study that menu, and one thing she's noticed is that you can have Indian tea or China tea. So when the waiter comes up with the pot and starts performing his functions, she says:

'Is that India or China?'

'It's tea, Madam,' he says.

'Oh,' says the lady, and blushingly opens her individual pot of jam.

I've already got down to work. So that pretty soon I'm asking for more bread.

'More bread?' says the waiter.

'More bread,' I say.

'More bread coming up,' he says. We've already established a communication, we two. It's heartening.

I demolish the supplementary bread, pour myself a last cup of tea, and settle back in my seat.

'It's been a lovely day,' says the Englishwoman.

'It has that,' I say.

'The hills look beautiful,' she says.

'Ay, they are beautiful hills,' I say, giving her her money's worth.

'Are you going home on holiday?' she says.

'No,' I say. 'I have just been on a long, long holiday, and now I am returning to work.'

'May I ask what your work is?'

'I'm a golf course attendant,' I say.

'Oh, how nice,' she says. She'd have said the same thing if I'd said I was a lavvy attendant.

'A lot of balls,' I say.

'What?' says the Englishwoman.

'I say there's always a wheen balls knocking about, you know, the wee white balls that they knock about, and that they try to put into the ground, you know, the wee hole in the ground.'

'Oh yes,' says the Englishwoman.

'Of course the hole must be as wee as the ball is wee,' I say.

'You understand. There are, as you might say, varying degrees of weeness. A great many people think that wee is always wee. But there is wee, and there is wee-wee,' I say.

'Oh, yes,' says the Englishwoman, faintly.

'Are *you* going on holiday, Madam?' I say.

'Oh yes,' she says. 'I'm going to stay with some friends.'

'Might I enquire whereabouts, Madam?' I say.

'In Largs,' says the Englishwoman.

'Largs,' I say, and then sombrely: 'Largs.'

'Do you know Largs?' she says.

'Madam, I was born there. Just on the north side of Kelburn.'

'Oh, Kelburn estate!'

'No, Madam, Kelburn golfcourse. And the first thing I saw when I opened my eyes was a wee white ball.'

At this, I give her a big, beaming smile, excuse myself, and go back to my mooly compartment.

12

Approaching Glasgow, approaching Glasgow ... Mile after mile of scabby factory ground. Wishaw—Colville's Basic Slag Works—Motherwell—Uddingston—Polmadie ...

> *Napoleon was a mighty man*
> *a mighty man was he*
> *he sailed right up the Geddes burn*
> *and captured Polmadie*

A crowd of plastered Scots come lurching up the corridor with a bleary-eyed female at their head, who says:

'Look, boys—Belsen.'

TIME ON A DARK RIVER

'Oh' he says, 'I got a map.'
'A map?' I says.
'Sure,' he says, 'I got a map
dat tells me about all dese
places. I take it wit me every
time I come out heah,' he says.

Thomas Wolfe

I

Today the packing-case containing my books arrived from
Liverpool. It had come over in the s.s. *Karin* from Bordeaux, and
had spent some time under rain in the Liverpool docks. When I
opened it, I found the books covered with a dark green fungus. I
scraped and rubbed off the fungus and stacked the books in what
a few days ago was a coal cellar. The packing-case itself was a
hefty thing, and when the haulers helped me to carry it up to the
house, we strained under the weight of it. One of them asked me
if it contained rifles. He was an Irishman. The other asked me if it
wasn't dead bodies. He was a Scotsman. Myself, I was wondering
if it didn't contain a chunk of the moon. I'm a Chinaman.

At eight or thereabouts I go down to the Maharajah Stores
for something to eat. On the way I pass the Hong Kong
Foodhouse—we're a cosmopolitan crowd up here on the hump
of the world. Mrs Maharajah is a real Indian with a shawl and a
pearl in her nose. When you ask for biscuits, she says: Wat you
want, biscot? Mr Maharajah is big and tall, with a sinister squint
in his eye, and says: toodle-oo. I come out with biscuits and a
pomegranate; but I leave the biscuits alone and make do with
the pomegranate. The biscuits were foosty; I shall eat no more.

The pomegranate was rotten.

2

Sunday afternoon.

One of those holy, obknoxious Sundays such as there are fifty-two a year in this god-forsaken place, and to while away the weary time (big, dutiful clocks all over the cancerous landscape), I go for a walk along the docks, coming down Byres Road, then along Dumbarton Road, then, in Argyll Street, taking the old Kelvinhaugh way down to the river, arriving at Kelvinhaugh Ferry. I cross the river on the ferry, then re-cross, and then re-cross again (the river quiet, the sky a soft grey, the ships berthed in great tranquillity) till the ferryman says to me:

'Are ye enjoyin' yersel?'

Crossing and re-crossing the old Clud on the ferry on that grey afternoon, watching the river-flow and the gulls. After ten or so crossings and re-crossings, I move away along Queen's Dock.

There the smell is strange, and yet vaguely familiar. Whisky—thousands of barrels lined there along the quay filled with sourmash bourbon whisky from Kentucky, USA, with, further on, a load of rye from Indiana. All those barrels, and drunken gulls swooping and yelling over them.

Here and there, too, along the docks, sitting on piles of rope or timber, wee men with bunnets and coloured mufflers reading pink newspapers.

Glasgow. Glasgow.

3

In the early dawn:

She rides a red horse
up Sauchiehall Street

'See you in Tibet'
she says

and disappears
into a smoky shebeen
down by the docks

4

Night at Charing Cross, standing at the foot of Hill Street there, wondering where to go and what to do. I see a plaque on a railing:

Rudolph Steiner Centre
Inquiries Welcome

So I decide to go and make inquiries. I push open the gate, enter the gas-lit close, climb to the first floor, see no Rudolph Steiner Centre, continue up to the second floor, and there I see two doors, still no Rudolph Steiner Centre, but on the wall next to one of the doors, I see written in thick pencil the word: Otto (German, like Rudolph, I'm getting hot), so I ring the bell, and then, no answer forthcoming, ring the bell again, which brings an old woman to the door:

'Excuse me,' I say, 'I'm looking for the Rudolph Steiner Centre.'

She looks at me as if I'd said I was looking for Rudolph the Red-Nosed Reindeer. Then:

'It's not here,' she says, 'It's down the stair. And it's not open on a Sunday.' She says Sunday with a religious knell in her voice.

'I'm sorry for troubling you, then,' I say.

'Oh, it's quite all right,' she says. 'Only it's a *Sunday*, you should have known, and it's late, it's nearly ten o'clock.'

'As late as that,' I say, 'I'm sorry. Good night.'

Ten o'clock. I go back down the stairs. This time I see a small brown plaque on one of the doors. I ring, just in case. No answer.

Ten o'clock. I continue up Hill Street. Quiet up there. Only an occasional television set shining coldly-blue in some of the big windows. As I walk, I look into the basement kitchens: an old man sitting at a table in semi-darkness with a cup of tea before him; in another, there's just a big bushy orange cat sitting on a table among the crockery, all alone in its glory.

Then, on the pavement before me, chalked in large letters, I see this rhyme:

I am a mole
and I live in a hole

Along Hill Street, then down into Woodlands Road, then finally I'm in Otago Lane North, at the edge of the River Kelvin, just under the flashing advert for Red Hackle Whisky. I stand there in the out-and-in flashing light, and watch its reflection on the dirty old Kelvin. I stand there for a long while, then I begin to do a bit of a dance, all on my oney-o, singing to myself:

Let the Midnight Special shine her light on me.
Let the Midnight Special shine her ever-lovin light on me . . .

5

I wasn't born in that house, but all my earliest memories are attached to it. I knew it was in Nielston, but I had only a very vague idea of its exact location. I took a bus for Nielston in Clyde Street, hoping I might find it.

I come off at the bus-terminus in Nielston, and recognize nothing. It's late on in the afternoon. There are few people in the streets, but I hear shouts now and then from the football pitch.

I stand undecided at first. Beyond the area of new houses, the hills stretch bare and cold. I wonder if I shouldn't go straight out to them and forget the house. But at length I go down into the old town.

Coming down the main street I see, down a side-lane, a set of railway signals, and I follow this. My father was a signalman in Nielston at that time, and I know the house was near the tracks. This path brings me to the station; but again I recognise nothing. I look round for a while, but there are no signs at all. Everything non-committal, meaningless. It seems the house is lost for good. Impossible to ask directions. 'Do you know the house where I used to live?' Absurd. 'Who are you?' It's only by following out the signs myself I'll find anything. But there are no signs, not the slightest one. The building opposite the station has blind windows, old and dilapidated, and nailed on its wall is a notice: British Legion.

I've almost given up, when it strikes me that the station here is Nielston High. There must, then, be a Nielston Low. Perhaps the Low one will be my source.

I enquire of two young lads at the corner if there is a Nielston Low, and if so where it is. The station exists. They tell me to go back up the main street, and cut down to the right by Toni's Chipshop.

November, Saturday, four o'clock and the shadows beginning to gather. I cut down Holehouse Brae. 'D'ye know the Mull?' the lads had asked. I had said I knew no mill—'Ye'll pass it anyway on the road doon'—but once here on Holehouse Brae, I think I recognise it vaguely, but only very vaguely.

It's only when I stand in Lochlibo Road that I feel I'm near the place, yet the house I see before me still has no meaning.

I stand there, and look over to the cold hills and the black branched trees on the sky-line, and then I see a flight of wild geese travelling southwards. It's well and truly winter now. I feel the coldness eating into me, and the geese flying out of sight there down the sky. I stand there with the factory looming up behind me, and then my eyes are caught by the gas-lamps being lit in the station, and then past the station, along behind a wall, I see a grey inconspicuous house, and I know that's it. It's by the side of the line, and I recognise the path leading down to the station, and I recognise the garden, though it's smaller than I had imagined. I think too I recognise the cold hills and copses behind it.

This is the house, isolated from the rest of Nielston, beside the railway-track, with only the hills behind it. I walk round about it, not remembering much, just glad to be there.

The sky is red now in the west, and through the black entanglement of the trees is a wonder to see. Such soft and multiple skies there are here on this seaboard, skies turned inside out, like a fur-lined glove. I stand there quiet, with the grey house, red sky, black trees, then I turn away suddenly and begin to walk back up the brae. I'm thinking of nothing, but a bit of an old Irish poem is in my head:

Crimson the bracken
it has lost its shape
the wild goose has raised
its accustomed cry.

I come back to my room in Glasgow.

6

Wiiiiiiind
nd
staaaaaaaars
nd
wiiiiiiind
nd
staaaaaaaars

the day's born deid

7

I continue flinging crazily about the city.

Today, fog and drizzle. A smoky, leaden indistinguishable mass. The river a wide, misty, empty-looking expanse.

Saturday—I've been through the markets of Shipbank Lane: *The Bonanza, Paddy's, The Popular, The Jolly, The Cosy, The Super* . . . In the lane, on the cobbles running with dirt, a fire is burning.

I go over the bridge into South Portland Street: dark-grey tenements lining a wide, empty roadway: thousands of uniform windows bare or with a dismal rag of curtain—pale faces behind them. Also dark faces. For many Pakistanis live here—witness the *Kashmir Butcher*, the *Pak Store*, the *Ravi Traders*, the *Wali Dairy*.

South Portland Street continues into Abbotsford Place, in the middle of which is a pub called *The Rising Sun* and at the end of which, in Turriff Street, is the *Glasgow Talmud Society*, and the *Glasgow Maccabi Association.*

Other institutions of the area: *The Medical Missionaries, The Muslim Mission, The Church of Baptized Believers.*

The Gorbals. Ancestral grounds. All the ghosts.

I find myself in Portugal Street.

There's a play park there, a monstrosity of a play park. A pond, full of bricks and old plaster. An underground cavern of brick, on the outside of which, painted with whitewash, you can read: 'Paddy, you mancit bastard. Buddha. Itali.' There are five thick poles too, with a conglomeration of dirty, frayed rope festooned around them. The ground is beaten earth, uneven, strewn with bricks and bottles. The whole surrounded by a high wire fence.

The building opposite deserted—all the windows smashed, except three, in which there is a pale light shining.

It's half past two. Time for 'Bright Hour' at the *Medical Missionaries.*

I go into the *Oriental Café*, round from Kidston Street. When I was a kid, if I remember rightly, this café was called *Joe's*. The Gorbals have been orientalized.

I drink a coffee, eat a chocolate biscuit; and then start walking again—up to the Gushetfaulds, then down into Eglinton Street . . .

I'm still walking when night falls.

8

Queen Street station
fog swirling round the newspapers
a voice booming
arrivals and departures
lonely o lonely
then the train
the countryside of darkness
the blue rain
and the screeching
of yellow stations on the way
and then at Falkirk
by the gate
that girl
in the fawn tight-belted raincoat
black hair
her eyes
her eyes rain falling countryside
how many times

9

West Café ... Southern Café ... New Bridge Café ... Bluebird
Café ....
  If I settle anywhere now, with the least chance of
concentration, it's in one or other of the most unfrequented cafés
of the city where I sit in the gloom and go through my crazy
meditations.

  I'm walking down Buchanan Street, with darkness falling. In
Renfield Street the starlings in their thousands are squealing
frantically.

  I go down to the river and cross it, but stop for a while on
the bridge watching the reflections of the city lights in the oil-

black waters, watching the grey-snow bank where a dog is loping about and howling into the night.

Over on the Gorbals side, I stop—rain is beginning to fall, turning the remaining snow into slush—in the *Southern Café*. I once wrote a short story in there, it was called *South Side Suicide* (a very euphonious title, no?) but that was a long time ago, when I still told myself stories. Now it's more a kind of geography I do.

Out of the *Southern Café*, I turn into South Portland Street, intending to maybe spend an hour in the Gorbals library, but the place is closed (I've forgotten it's one of those damned Sundays). So I walk up Portland Street, and come upon a large building with smoky-yellow lighted windows where on a plaque, with difficulty deciphered in the murky dark, can be read that this institution was founded by Isaac Wolfe. I climb up the stair of the building and push open the door: a vast room, bare but for benches round the walls and a serving counter down the middle. A few men seated round the walls look up as I come in. The other thing that attracts immediate attention is the great star of Israel painted at eye level on a partition just inside the door. *Mishpochah—mazeltov!*

I come back out into the cold, wet darkness.

And go back up to the *Bluebird Café*, near Queen's Park, where I drink a coffee and eat a sandwich. The rain is falling thickly now over the city, over my old moon city, and it is Sunday night in the winter of my soul.

From Queen's Park I walk to Pollockshaws, another two miles or so, maybe three, and then retrieve my steps down the same monotonous road, back into the Gorbals where I take my last repose in the *New Bridge Café*, and then cross the bridge hearing seagulls over the river screaming in the darkness.

10

About to draw the blinds
I see over the rooftops
and the ten thousand chimneys
with the night-fog
settling down over the city
a dark, red sun.

11

It is almost the end of the winter, the month of March. The grey sky is mottled with blue and where the sun is curdled in cloud, a pale burning yellow. In the city the stronghold of a bank has been raided, and a murder trial is about to begin. It is the month of March. We are waiting.

On the suspension bridge over the river, the people wait, loiter and watch, for the old Clud is being dredged—a rust-red dredger by the name of *Sir William H. Raeburn* is anchored in the stream with a hawser attached to a capstan on the quay for extra security, and is dredging, dropping its heavy iron maw into the river with a splash, letting it descend with a rattling chain, raising it again with mud and water dripping from its cracks, and swinging it round in a half-circle, depositing the sludge in the hold. Already the *Sir William H. Raeburn* is lying low in the water, the plimsoll mark eight. The people stand on the bridge, me among them, and watch.

On the bridge there are comings and goings, but always a knot of loiterers who watch the dredger and, perhaps, hear the cold clamours of the seagulls, people with time to spare. But there is one who sits darkly with his right leg under him beside a chalk circle in which is written: *God blessed you.* And the passers-by, reading the phrase, wonder: when? Either that man has made a mistake, meaning to write the more common: God bless you, or he is being very, very subtle. Subtle or no, as people pass without giving him a tosser, he curses them, and prolongs his curses so that he has just finished with one customer when another turns up.

There is quietness here on the river—only the cursing voice at the centre of the bridge now, and now and then the screech of a gull, and the dull chain-rattle of the dredger. There is a pale blue mist in the air, deeper, concentrated under the bridges, while from St Enoch's station come puffs and billows of white smoke that dissipate themselves calmly into the sky. It is the month of March and there is a quietness.

I stand there on the bridge taking it all in, watching the people pass: the Pakistani woman in the orange dress, the drunk Scot in the green suit mumbling to himself, the wee man with the black coat fastened with pins shuffling along in a hen-toed gait, and then I break away and go to St Enoch's station where, on the concourse, there are more people sitting on the benches waiting for their trains. And I wonder if that blue-lit *Enquiry Office* could answer the really big question which is forming somewhere vaguely in the depths of my mind, but which I can't yet formulate (it will remain a lump in my throat, inarticulate as love, and perhaps it is a kind of love).

With all the details gone, what remains in my mind is smoke, or mist: smoke rising spirally and quietly from fantastic chimneys, smoke hanging over the proletarian city, or the first mists of spring rising up from the wet earth as the sun's heat grows in strength and comes closer. The beginning and the end is smoke. Acrid smoke, bringing tears to the eyes.

I go back to the bridge. The *Sir William H. Raeburn* is still dredging, and the people are still watching, and the beggar is still cursing. I stand there, with the bridge gently swaying under me, and look over the city to the sun that, disengaged now from the misty cloud, is gleaming white in a ring of red fire . . ..

It is the month of March, and we are waiting.

THE ROCKY ROAD TO CARRAROE

*Well, now you know or don't you kennet or
haven't I told you every telling has a taling.*

James Joyce

I

There weren't many passengers that spring night on the Dublin
boat. As I stood on the deck when we were already a good way
down the river, after having left Anderston Quay, Glasgow, in
the purple fogs of evening, as I stood there by the rail listening
to the seagulls in the big mauve darkness, the only other people
on deck were a bunch of bottle-swinging mashers and herries
getting ready to spend a happy vomiting night of it. I waited up
there till we were past Gourock, and into the open, then I went
down to my bunk and settled into my Irish green blankets for
sleep. I'd just spent one of the craziest winters of my life in
Glasgow, but I felt very good lying there in those blankets,
good and warm and at my ease, and began dozing off with a
line of Whitman's in my head: '. . . out of the cradle endlessly
rocking . . .' I'd been away from poetry and everything else alive
for months, and the fact that I could feel inside a poem again
this way kind of reassured me. I wasn't completely lost. 'We are
all lost here in America, but I know we shall find ourselves
again.' That was Thomas Wolfe . . . In the big America-Russia
of our age . . . We are all Americano-Russians or Russo-
Americans . . . But I was going to Ireland—What was Ireland?
. . . It was maybe (it suits me to say so) with this question-no-
answer on my mind that I fell asleep.

2

According to an Irish poet, over Dublin and its river 'the sun comes up in the morning like barley-sugar'. Well, that morning as we came up the Liffey, the barley-sugar had kind of melted a bit in the drizzling rain, and what remained by way of light was a diffused dusky yellowness, out of which rose Dublin for all the world like another Glasgow, so that my spirits were slightly dampened and my hopes slightly crushed, not to speak of the soiling of illusions I didn't have, when my foot touched for the first time the stones of Holy Mother Ireland at the end of the gang-plank. And as, in one of the dark dock streets, a Co-op cab was waiting for a passenger, I obliged by getting into it and moved off in the direction of St Stephen's Green, which was the first locality that came into my head. And there it was, after rolling through the drizzly streets, lanes and alleys, and paying 'five bobbies' to the long-coated and incredibly ugly cabman, the Green, where I walked about for a while and the seedy ghost of James Joyce (Ireland is a helluva literary country) singing a song beside me, something like 'Bless this House', but which ended up in a phrase of some hideous and outrageously garboyled jargon that was an offence not only to the King's English but also to the Pope's Irish, and must have been the lingo of Beelzebub himself before the world got all rationalized and sad.

But soon I was feeling hungry, so I quit the ghost stuff, and wandered around for a while in my hungry flesh, till I came across this big *Oriental Café* into which I entered, into its murky light full of the smell of coffee and the spice of buns, and sat down on a red plush bench, with a great wooden headpiece rising at my back, and all around me the oriental wallpaper and the many-coloured plate-glass windows, and ordered coffee, cream, butter and buns. By God, it was a strange place, a real sight for sore eyes, but it pleased me to be there in that dim old nineteenth-century baroque retreat, watching the antics of an old fellow looking like the Taoist god of longevity snuggling up to a young fur-coated woman who edges away from him and finally protests, to which he protests that 'the seat's not reserved', at which she gets up with her coffee and moves to another place, leaving him with his filthy coat and his red rheumy eyes and his desolation. Ah—and over there a Bloom-like character with his mouth full of bun is examining the 'Love Map of Ireland' in *The People*. The Love Map of Ireland—with the northern part of the country striped in black. There's apparently no love in an Orangeman.

Talking of Orangemen, and the rest of the dissenting Five-per-Cent, when I left the doomsday café, and resumed my explorations of Dublin's fair city in the morning, I saw a plaque on a doorway and on the plaque was engraved the information that behind this door was quartered the *Incorporated Association for the Relief of Distressed Protestants*, while next to it was another intimating the presence of *Kilroy's College*—so that's where the bugger came from? Dublin, the name of a 'fair city', was beginning to take on a grotesque substantiality. I was beginning to like it.

3

And I continued liking it the next couple of days, during which, having found myself a room at the *Hanrahan Hotel* in Harcourt Street, I went fishing the Dublin streets for images: a peach tree struggling into blossom in the grounds of Trinity College; the pale faces of long and slender girls passing up and down O'Connell Bridge. And sat in the thick warmth of pubs. And hunted for old books in the second-hand bookshops along the river. And sat late at night in my room with the red-tree wallpaper reading Irish poetry. But it was not only, and not even mainly, Dublin I had come for in Ireland, I wanted to go over west, into Connaught, the Gaeltacht, which is why, on the afternoon of the third day after my arrival in Dublin, I was out on the road to Galway, with a bottle of Irish Mist in my rucksack and a foosty-looking box of Black Magic chocolates, looking for a ride. And it came, the ride, right across Ireland, to Castlebar in the County Mayo.

I enjoyed that journey—the rolling of the car through dark boggy lands under the drizzling and then pouring rain, but most of all I enjoyed the talk of the man who was driving it, good, rich, high talk such as I had not been able to indulge in for a long time. He was full of anecdotes concerning books and writers, this man, and had a deep, richly human appreciation of writers and writing which was a delight to listen to. It was 'character' he liked in a writer and writing—'he was a great character', he'd say—but deeper even than the appreciation of character was his love, even his reverence, for genius—'he was a strange genius of a man'. It was personal substance he was looking for all the time. No thin theories—he told me the story of Brendan his friend Behan who, asked if he would describe his writing as futuristic, replied with truculent candour: 'what the fuck is futurism,' or words to that effect. 'He was probably elephants too,' added my friend Kevin, 'he was nearly always elephants.' And he told me of Patrick Kavanagh lecturing at Trinity College, also elephants. And then there was St John Gogarty, a marvellous talker and a humorous devil, who wrote a beautiful poem of eulogy to Britain and her armies during the '14–'18 war, a poem for which he was highly commended and I'm not sure if he wasn't even awarded a medal, but the lines of which began, so it was later discovered, with carefully chosen letters, which arranged in line spelt this: 'The whores will be busy.' Since, too, we were making for the County Mayo:

> *Towards the Eve of St. Brigit the days will be growing*
> *The cock will be crowing and a home-wind shall blow*
> *And I never shall stop but shall ever be going*
> *Till I find myself roving through the County Mayo*

we talked much of Raftery, the blind minstrel from the County Mayo, whom I knew I'd find more traces of in the County Galway, where most of his later wanderings took place, and I told brother Kevin how I'd first come across the name of

Raftery in a book of verse that contained a wonderful translation by Padraic Fallon of Raftery's famous poem 'Mary Hynes', and how from that reference, I came to borrow, through the intermediary of an Irish acquaintance, Douglas Hyde's book on Raftery from the Irish consulate in Paris where I was then living. 'You're an amazing sort of off-beat fellow,' said Kevin, and, for the first time in ten months, I felt a little pleased with myself.

And so it went on, from Raftery to Synge, and to Daniel Corkery's book on Synge, and to some of the phrases in it that I liked, such as this: 'Ireland is a passionate country: like the face of a passionate man it is either dull and expressionless or else ablaze with vision,' or this: '. . . the bleakness and intensity that we always find in Irish literature at its best. . . .' And then as we were passing Mullingar, scene of the fair in Joyce's *Ulysses*, brother Kevin began to quote from that 'chaffering allincluding most farraginous chronicle,' evoking adventures of the 'lovelorn longlost lugubru Booloohoom,' finishing with Bloom's apotheosis, which goes hilariously and preposterously so: 'And they beheld Him even Him, ben Bloom Elijah, amid clouds of angels ascend to the glory of the brightness at an angle of forty-five degrees over Donohoe's in Little Green Street like a shot off a shovel.' That 'forty-five degrees' kills me.

It was a great talk. And when it came to an end, too soon, at Castlebar, we took leave of each other exchanging addresses and promising to write letters till the next time we met in Ireland.

It was Saturday night, and I slept the night there in Castlebar, in the County Mayo, prepared the next morning to hike or hitch-hike down through the Connemara hills to Lettermullan or Carraroe, and maybe then be able to get a turf-boat to take me out to the Aran Islands.

4

Next morning, then, Sunday, I was out of Castlebar, and on the road to Westport. I had walked halfway along it when a car stopped, with a couple making for the chapel in Westport, and took me into town, where I made for a hotel and a bit of breakfast. I was sitting in the hotel lounge drinking coffee and eating arrowroot biscuits when a dozen or so young men invaded the place from the dining-room, after a communal breakfast discussing politics, and settled themselves on armchairs and couches, evoking past campaigns: 'We went through them like a dose of salts'; 'Did you see her coming down there with her cavalcade of bully-boys like a blidy Boadicea'; 'And Michael bloody well Patmore he says to MacLuskey "up wit yer mits" he says'—and preparing a new one. I left after about a quarter hour, but it was enough to know that Irish local politics is a pretty colourful and explosive mixture.

It was a fine morning on the road:

My thanks, for this fresh April
for the blue crisp waters
and the golden grasses
for the open roads
and her breasts in the wind

and I was happy walking there, especially round that little loch with the shining blue waters and the long golden grass, and the wind blowing gustily over it. I must have been about five or six miles from Westport on the road to Leenane when a car came by going down the way to Clifden. It was a man and his wife were in the car, and he started talking about Craogh Patrick which we could see from the road, and how there was a stone up there with the mark of St Patrick's knee, and how St Patrick up there had dumped all the snakes of Ireland into the sea, and how 'one of the loveliest things you'll see' is the torchlight pilgrimage up the holy mountain on the last Sunday in July.'

Intending to walk down through the Twelve Ben country by Loch Inagh, I left St Patrick's car at Kylemore and set off across the moorland, where for the next three hours the only living things I saw were wind-ruffled red-marked sheep and a

Connemara pony who didn't bray a single patriotic word but just looked at me out of big brown eyes.

It was coming on evening, and a cold wind blowing when, just before the place called Recess, a car picked me up, going down to Galway by way of Maam Cross, Screebe, and Costelloe. When I told the driver of my intention to try and get a turf boat down at Carraroe, he began talking of the people down there (I remembered what Synge had said of 'the half-savage temperament of Connaught'), telling me of the local feuds that often get settled at the dances—'the country's dance-mad'— where 'they fight dirty and tough', and 'you might see somebody get split'. But, no, I wouldn't see anybody get split, because the time was Lent, and 'by the grace of the bishops of Ireland' there are no dances in Lent.

I left that car at O'Flaherty's Bar, with a couple of miles' walk to get down to the village of Carraroe.

It was going on dark grey night now, and as I walked down through that rocky end-world, with now and then a stocky pale-gleaming cottage and piles of turf all along the rock wall lining the road, and the black sea rushing in the darkness, I was beginning to regret the sun and the wind and the clarity of the afternoon. It's a place of stones, down there, a most fantastic place of stones, and if Renan was right when he said that 'the stone . . . seems the natural symbol of the Keltic races,' I was in the midst of Keltic landscape with a vengeance.

At Carraroe itself, I went to the grocery-post office to ask about the possibilities of lodging. The kind woman there made several phone-calls, but most of the places that receive guests in the season—the area is invaded by students of Gaelic—were not yet ready. Finally, however, I was to be fixed up with a Mr Jim McGlone who, at present attending a concert in the village hall, would turn up at the pub in a couple of hours' time. So I went to the pub.

There I spent a warm and pleasant time with three old-timers huddled round the fire, only one of whom, and the most garrulous, had the English; the same asked me if I didn't have the Irish, and when I said no, he said it was just as well, because they spent their time cursing each other. Well, the fire blazed, we exchanged drinks and cigarettes, and talked, my friend with the English sometimes translating a remark from the two Gaelic men, he himself telling me of his experiences in the army, until he said to me, 'D'ye know the bad man's song?' and when I again avowed my ignorance, he said it was 'Time, Gentlemen, Please', and it very soon was.

It was then Jim McGlone turned up, not from any village concert, but from next door where he'd been playing darts, a brutish-looking sort of fellow, and I accompanied him to see in his house the room I was to have. Leaving me in his kitchen (his wife I think was still at the concert), at a littered table, with before me a plate of old meat sandwiches, one of which had two mouthfuls missing—'At my place you get a good feed'—he went, by his way of it, to get the room ready.

It was a mess, the room, when I finally saw it, with face-powder strewn over the dressing-table, shoes scattered on the floor, a pair of wilted pyjamas lying on a chair, and the bedsheets no more attractive than the sandwiches, obviously slept in not only the night before but many a night before that. He waxed indignant and abusive when I declined his hospitality. What did I expect for twenty-five shillings? And I wasn't to think I'd find anywhere else to sleep in Carraroe, begorrah, no, and when I came back to him, the price would be doubled. He was a very accommodating fellow. I left his happy home, and the door banged behind me. Outside, it was pitch dark, and it was raining. I made off in the direction of a guest house I'd seen advertised on the street.

When I arrived there, I saw light in a window, but when I rang there was no reply. So I rang again, and shouted up at the window, but still there was no reply. 'The boogars are deef,' I said to myself, and went to the bungalow next door, where there was also a light (maybe crammed full of deaf Irishmen, I thought), to enquire what was up and why the guest house turned a dull ear to prospective guests. At the bungalow, my bell-ringing got a response. A man came cautiously to the door and told me that the owner of the guest house was up at the concert and would no doubt be down very shortly. So I thanked him and went back to my post. It was damned cold, what with the wind and the rain, and I was also feeling hungry. At length, however, a car drew up, was parked on the other side of the road, and I was just waiting for the woman who now appeared to come up to the door of the guest-house where I was, when I realised she was making for the bungalow. False hope. I hunched down beside the stairs out of the wind. Then somebody else turned up. The police. In the person of one burly specimen who was curious to know who I was and what I was up to. I told him I wanted into the guest house, and that I was waiting for the owner who, I'd been told at the bungalow next door, was up at the concert.

'Oh, but the concert's been out this good half-hour,' he said.

'Well, she must be with friends or something,' I said.

'That's strange,' he said.

I waited. There was after all a chance that he would invite me along to the constabulary.

'Did you not see a car coming down here?' he continued.

'I did,' I said, 'but the woman who got out of it went into the bungalow next door.'

'That's the owner, that's her,' he said.

'But she saw me standing here,' I said, 'and the man in that bungalow knows I'm waiting here.'

'That's strange,' he said.

I waited for him to put his next two and two together. Either invite me to the constabulary, or come with me to the bungalow next door.

'You'll have to do something,' he repeated, and putting his leg over his bicycle and pushing off, left me with the recommendation:

'Action! Action!'
and I never saw him again.

I went back to the bungalow, asked to speak with the owner of the guest house who I'd been told was there, and was informed by her from behind the door, which wasn't even opened, that she wasn't going to open the guest house for me at this time of night. Hospitable bastards. I told them what I thought of them.

But that didn't give me a place to sleep. I began to wonder if I'd better not spend the night walking on into sweet Galway Bay. Going down through the village, however, I decided to try this other house I saw with a light in it. A man came to the door, and he was listening to my story and request when his wife came up behind him and said curtly, 'we don't take lodgers,' and then disappeared again. The man had just time to tell me there was another house up the road might put me up before his wife bitchily called him in. Knowing this was going to be my last effort, I went to the house he'd mentioned, and after explaining all the circumstances again, got a room and a bed there, for which I was grateful, though they were both damp as hell, and went to sleep half-dressed, with my pullover still on my back, cursing and shivering.

5

At eight or so next morning I was out again in the village waiting for the bus to Galway. The rain was still falling. I knew I wouldn't be going to the Aran Islands after all, Carraroe was enough (there were no turf boats anyway at this time of the year, the old-timers had told me), and as I stood there taking a last good look at Carraroe I was pretty sure that the phrases Synge uses to describe the islands were exactly applicable to these stony grounds also—'a mass of wet rock, a strip of turf, and then a tumult of waves.' And that morning there at Carraroe was like the fog-weather Synge found on Inishmore—

'the same grey obsession twining and wreathing itself among the narrow fields, and the same wail from the wind that shrieks and whistles in the loose rubble of the walls.'

After a night in a damp bed, I was ready to leave this desolation, and was glad to board that Galway bus. During the journey, to pass the time, and to get the night's experience out of my system, I scribbled down:

The Curse of Carraroe

*Carraroe is in Ireland
in the district of Connemara
full of people with names
like Flaherty Murphy O'Hara*

*But above all there's one McGlone
whose Christian name is Jim
from Galway away to Athlone
there isn't a moron like him*

*Mick Nolan's the name of the guard
a hopeless excuse for a man
if I were an Irish bard
I'd turn him into a hen*

*Then there's that bitch O'Leary
Christian right to the core
turn up at her place late and weary
she won't even open the door*

*That's maybe enough for one day
though I surely could add to the list
(for example O'Neill and O'Shea)
but I think you get the gist*

On Carraroe and its people
to conclude I say this curse
may they all drop dead in their chapel
and roast in hell or worse

6

And so to Galway, that 'grey city of stone and mist and water' as Padraic Fallon calls it. Galway, where I settled into a room in a good hotel, for warmth and comfort and, lying down on the bed—outside the rain had not slackened—reread my notes on Raftery, just to get myself into the mood of the place; and stood later by the Corrib river, soaked to the skin, watching the fishermen; and walked out to the end of the breakwater with Galway behind me drenched in spray; and hunted in a fine bookshop for an old book or two; and went up to Galway University library to get myself looked down upon for not having the Irish (now can I help it if practically the only Gaelic I ever heard spoken was '*Slanjy va*' or something like that slithered on the tongues of rid biddy drinkers in the Q-Irish city of Glasgow?); and then finally, got out on the road again, in the direction of Kiltartan and Ballylee, as writ the said Raftery:

> *That Sunday, on my oath, the rain was a heavy overcoat*
> *On a poor poet, and when the rain began*
> *In fleeces of water to buckleap like a goat*
> *I was only a walking penance reaching Kiltartan*
> *And there, so suddenly that my cold spine*
> *Broke out on the arch of my back in a rainbow*
> *This woman surged out of the day with so much sunlight*
> *I was nailed there like a scarecrow . . .*

That woman was, of course, the famous Mary Hynes (an old fiddler, not Raftery this time, another one, said of her: 'Mary Hynes was the finest thing that was ever shaped') whose praises Raftery sings in his song:

For Mary Hynes, rising, gathers up there
Her ripening body from all the love stories
And, rinsing herself at morning, shakes her hair
And stirs the old gay books in libraries
And what shall I do with sweet Boccacio?
And shall I send Ovid back to school again
With a new heading for his copybook
And a new pain?

and whose presence in Ballylee, especially after it had been sung by Raftery turned that obscure little hamlet into a place known throughout all the west of Ireland and further. As Raftery writes himself with extravagant humour:

If I praised Ballylee before it was only for the mountains
Where I broke horses and ran wild
And not for its seven crooked smoky houses
Where seven crones are tied
All day to the listening top of a half door
And nothing to be heard or seen
But the drowsy dropping of water
And a gander on the green

But, boys! I was blind as a kitten till last Sunday
This town is earth's very navel!
Seven palaces are thatched there of a Monday
And O' the seven queens whose pale
Proud faces with their seven glistening sisters
The Pleiads, light the evening where they stroll
And one can find the well by their wet footprints
And make one's soul . . .

7

Ballylee, then, on a cold wet morning, with Raftery and Mary Hynes, coming out along the hedgy and stone-walled roads from Galway (a bit of the way in a lorry, and the rest on foot) looking,

after the rich words of the folk-poet and the famed beauty of the
woman, both of them factors which attracted the poet to this area:

> *Some few remembered still when I was young*
> *A peasant girl commended by a song*
> *Who'd lived somewhere upon that rocky place . . .*
> *Strange, but the man who made the song was blind . . . .*

for Yeats' tower, that ruin of a 'gaunt tower' which he
considered as 'a permanent symbol of my work plainly visible
to the passer-by. As you know, all my art theories depend on
just this—rooting of mythology in the earth':

> *An ancient bridge and a more ancient tower*
> *A farmhouse that is sheltered by its wall*
> *An acre of stony ground,*
> *Where the symbolic rose can break in flower,*
> *Old ragged elms, old thorns innumerable,*
> *The sound of the rain or sound*
> *Of every wind that blows;*
> *The stilted water hen*
> *Crossing stream again*
> *Scared by the splashing of a dozen cows . . .*
> *A winding stair, a chamber arched with stone,*
> *A grey stone fireplace, with an open hearth*
> *A candle and a written page . . .*

When I came to the tower that morning, drenched to the bones,
I found a representative of *Bord Failte* wrapped in tweeds and
huddled up against an electric heater, reading a book on Yeats,
waiting to show an expected party of visitors round the place.
By God, it was cold in that there tower—the guardian invited
me to share the heater with her, the first, she hoped, of more to
come, and we had a talk in which she recounted some anecdotes
concerning Yeats, while I listened and enjoyed the heat. Then
when the party came I wandered round the rooms myself and
ended up, while they were talking literature by the heater, sitting

in the fine big room above the stream, and quietly freezing.

From Thoor Ballylee, then, I got on to the Dublin road and was picked up before long by a laconic Irish-American who'd been everywhere, including Honolulu, and who had come to Ireland to settle down, in a cottage he had on the coast, called *The Stormy Rest*, which had thatch on the roof and green Connemara marble on the floor . . .

We got in to Dublin at seven o'clock, and that night, after walking round and round the streets again, I took the boat back over to Glasgow, composing, as we came back up the Clyde, this little poem:

Thud. Thud. Thud. Thud.
The boat coming up the river
Dead slow under the rain

That's how it was.

TRAVELS IN THE DRIFTING DAWN

Mind travelled in the north, towards the dark waters

Chuang Tzu

1

Morning of December 23rd, I'm up at five, pack my rucksack with a loaf, some apples, a change of socks, a towel, and make for Queen Street station—along Great Western Road, quiet, quiet, only from the far end of Bank Street, the noise of milk-crates, the streets frost-sparkling, Kelvinbridge humped in whiteness (smell of warm bread in the air), and board the 5.55 for Tarbet.

2

Dawn's beginning to break. A dark-blue drift in the night sky. I walk down to Arrochar, and continue round the loch. Daylight comes. Ice everywhere—hanging tusks, moulded jellyfish. A satin lustre on the rocks. Dawn wind chill—a newspaper blows by in the still semi-darkness. I go up into a wood, lie down under a fir tree, and eat my breakfast (an apple, a slice of bread).

When I come back onto the road, there's a lorry parked.

'Where are ye goin'?' says the driver.

'Inveraray.'

'Come on, a'll take ye part of th' way.' I climb up into the cabin with him.

We chug and rattle up the *Rest and Be Thankful*. I'm sitting on a hot tank that almost burns my backside off. Man starts talking:

'The black frost's a bugger,' he says, 'only one thing fur it—go slow.' We go slow. It's a long drag. I look at the hills. Massive and blunt, bulging, capped with snow and with ice that dribbles down to the valleys in gobs and streaks. There's a grey smoor clinging round the white-grey tops.

'Ye get tired lookin' at them,' says the driver.

We come to the crossroads. He's going to Dunoon or somewhere.

'Thanks.'

A black lochan, ice-gripped. Those black rocks. The ice streaming over them, clinging to them, jelly. Yellow grass. Red bracken.

Now at the top of Loch Fyne. Sand banks. Weed—a dead, ugly weed. Black, black, dismal waters. Seagulls keening in the wind.

Along Loch Fyne, the shore. I pick up a lump of quartz, put it in my rucksack. A beauty:

> *I walk on the shingle towards the town*
> *picking up here and there a gnarled stone*
>
> *I see a rock the colour of blood*
> *with dark weed matted on its head*
>
> *walking now faster into the wind*
> *the bitter cold gripping my hand.*

Look!—that cormorant skimming away there—black against the greydark—over the waters.

3

Approach to Inveraray:

> *Two fine bridges before you come to Inveraray*
> *at two in the afternoon maybe*

after walking twenty mile
and the wind blowing like hell

At the first fine bridge there are swans
and two old boats like skeletons
        while in the grey sky lost
        the sun drifts like a ghost

The town is just a hundred yards away
wind-buffeted and drenched with spray
        since our feet are no longer light
        we'll crawl in here for the night

4

The Temperance Hotel.
It's cold, it's freezing. I look down at the backyard. I sit on
the bed. Then there's a knock at the door, and a face appears:
'Oh, I thought there was no one in. It was just something I
wanted out the cupboard.'
She goes to the cupboard, and takes out one of the biscuit-
tins with which the thing is packed. So I'm in the room where
they store the biscuits. What else do they store here? It must be
their refrigerator. Maybe they're waiting till I freeze before they
cut me up. How about a little gallows' ballad to dance some
heat into my bones?

They stuck him with a kitchen knife
because he asked for heat
they've taken away that poor man's life
and fifteen shillings neat

Out of the wild and the wind he came
his possessions on his back
he asked at the inn if there was room
they answered: come in, mac

They put him with the brussels sprouts
in a room that was ten below
they gave him a bed that was made for smouts
and left it there to grow

You'll be all right there, they smiling said
and sidled out the door
the man lay dressed upon the bed
in case he should freeze to the floor

The air grew colder, hellish cold
till he could no longer stand it
he cried aloud to the whole household
by God, if you've heat, please send it

The devil heard him is my guess
hence the assassination
they found that poor man in a press
with a knife in his constitution

I go to the toilet. There's a notice pinned up there: 'Don't sit here, there's work to be done.' Back in my room. I'm trying to keep alive, when another knock comes at the door and a head appears. Somebody else at the biscuits. 'Just help yourself.' I add: 'I'm freezing.'

'Oh,' she says, 'come away down to the fire.'

I ask her if maybe when I come back up to sleep, I could have a heater.

'Oh, yes,' she says, 'and a bottle in your bed as well. All the boys get a bottle. Archie'll see to you.'

I go down to the living room, where there's a roaster burning in the grate. Supper's at six.

Just before six, the residents come in. A work-gang. Pylon-men and tunnelers. 'Rory's on it again,' they say.

'If he comes in tight tonight, he's out,' says Archie.

Supper.

'See that rice there, it's no hauf-cooked. It blows up twice that size in yer guts.'

Archie does the serving. Enter Hughie, the joker of the establishment. Two friends of his mentioned: Flossy Bumfluff and Midnight Mary. It's Hughie does the rounds with the hot water bottles.

I'm to get a call 'wi' the boys' at half past six.

5

Breakfast. Ham and eggs, tea and rolls. I talk with a lorry driver from Lesmahagoe. The black frost again. And with the load he's got. He'll take me up as far as Lochgilphead. He gets his flask of tea made up (six spoonfuls of sugar).

The lorry's hard to start. At last, he goes down to swing the handle while I press the starter. It works.

Down the road to Lochgilphead. Have to watch the camber. The lorry's meant to carry seven tons, and it's carrying nine. Weighs four tons itself. If it starts to coup, it won't stop.

It's a lonely road between Lochgair and Lochgilphead
early down the morning
the sky gravid with snow
a light blinking on the loch
a trawler out in the grey smoor
and the wind running fire along the grass and bracken
and the telegraph poles with their white cones
like signs in a language you do not know

twilight is a bad time for lorry drivers
the lamps are not much use
without their complement the darkness
and the light of day has not yet come
an uncertain time

especially if you're on a seven-ton lorry
with a nine-ton load
and the whole thing swinging like the devil
and the engine so weak
it wouldn't pull a fish out of water

6

Scripsit in Argyll Café, Lochgilphead. Hector and his mother. A customer:

'Four quarters o' big peppermints. Sorry to bother you Hector wi' the four quarters.'

'I've got a man buys two pounds a week.'

'You would think that widna be good for him.'

'Ay, I would think that tae.'

'I've heard McKellar the ARP man during the war bought seven pounds at a time.'

'By Christ, it must have been the nerves.'

Another customer, young woman:

'Jesus Christ, it's bloody cold,' says Hector.

'It wid freeze you.'

'Freeze whit?' says Hector.

'Oh, you know better than me,' says the girl.

'You're a comedian of a woman are you not,' says Hector's mother, and continues:

'See Barbara Stewart the son, he's come back to the Co-operative.'

'I've just been to buy a leek,' says the woman, and holds it up: '1/4.'

'1/4!' says Hector's mother.

'For a wee leek the size o' ma finger,' says the woman.

'A bloody bit o' grass,' says Hector.

'1/4!' says Hector's mother.

'Och, well, it's Christmas,' says Hector.

When Hector sees the postman coming, he starts singing:

There's no a team
like the Glasgow Rangers
No, no, not one.

'I think that's true,' says the postman with religious conviction, and hands over the mail. Hector's mother opens an envelope.

'Christmas cards,' she says. 'A've never seen her in thirty years, never sent her a Christmas card, an' she sends me one every year. It's a shame, hee-hee.'

'That's whit ye call a Christmas card relation,' says the postman.

'It's all Christmas, now,' says the mother. 'It used tae be the New Year.'

7.

I hitch a lorry up to Ardrishaig:

What a welter of seagulls
and a wind whetted by the Arctic
and the brown-and-green sea
cowping great masses of surf
over the rocks
while the Cretan of Glasgow
and the Halcyon of Irvine
are unloading coal . . .

From Ardrishaig to Tarbert. Up there, the nets are lying about in wispy piles, bracken-red and brown, and the mending's being done. The names of boats:

Brighter Morn
Our Lassie
Golden Chance
Caledonia
Dalriada . . .

I hitch a lorry going back to Lochgilphead. The sky's growing heavy and dark.

'That's the east wind blowin' the smoke over from Glasgow,' says the lorry driver.

8

In Lochgilphead, the main street branches off into two roads. The one leads to Oban and the other to the lunatic asylum. I take the one to Oban.

I've been walking for a while when a car stops, unsolicited: 'I wonder if you'd like a lift. You looked so independent striding along there.' I get in. She's a queer mixture, this woman, a cross between the lady-of-the-hall and the land-girl, her speech a mongrel blend of the most effete southern English and the most homespun Scotch. 'Ay,' she says every now and then, 'Ay, Ay.' The real doric touch. And the number of 'wee' things that enter her conversation is astounding. She tells me the old chemist at Lochgilphead was a jolly good fellow. Private concern, you know. Whereas the new thing's a multiple store, only intake considered. She likes the Lochgilphead shops, though, in general—they wrap your purchases in a nice bit of paper that doesn't have the name of the shop all over it . . . One of the English immigrants to the Highlands. Jolly old Scotland.

Kilmartin. I go down into the neolithic burial cairns. Walk round the stone circles also. Just-over-half moon in the sky. The light—yellow as of fire, and a dark-blue earthy light. This is my territory.

Sleep the night just outside Kilmartin.

'We don't hold Christmas here,' says the host.

'They're gettin too Englified,' says his wife.

9

The next day, before dawn, I'm on the Oban road:

Winter, and a wild wind, and I walk a dark road.
Dawn gathers like a pool of blood in the hollows
*   of the mountains.*

Then the sky opens the eye of its mouth.
From the black rocks, an icy lustre.
Fish of ice all along the shore.
Two gulls flying catch the first light, and gleam.

A dusky redness, about eight o'clock. I wash my feet in the loch. The telephone wires are howling.

At Kilmelford, I hitch a lorry collecting milk from the farms.

10

Oban. I go into a restaurant for a breakfast. Coffee and a scone. There's a school-master lives here, supposed to be great on Kierkegaard. I had been thinking of going to see him. Then just as I'm deciding not to bother making the visit, a man passes by outside under the rain, against a background of wheeling seagulls, wearing a black coat and a stiff, black hat, with a bit of beard wispy in the hat's shadow. It pleases me to think that must be the man. Walking about Oban the way Kierkegaard walked about Copenhagen.

But I feel so far away out on my own—among the neolithic rocks and the arctic seagulls—that I don't want to talk.

11

Late December by the Sound of Jura:

Red bracken on the hills
rain snow hail and rain
the deer are coming down
the lochs are gripped in ice
the stars blue and bright

I have tried to write to friends
but there is no continuing
I gaze out over the Sound
and see hills gleaming in the icy sun.

THE INHABITANT OF EDINBURGH

She's an allagrugous auld city in this allerish licht
Hugh MacDiarmid

I

Grey grey grey white grey grey black
grey white grey grey grey grey white grey
grey grey black grey grey

I was walking down by Cramond, having taken a No. 18 bus out from the city. 'Dull, wet day,' as the weather forecast chalked up on a blackboard outside a petrol-station had it—'Dull, wet day. But will probably clear up in the afternoon.' It was the back end of the afternoon, and there had been no clearing up. But in my room, after a bout of work and writing, I wanted to be near the sea, so I went to Cramond.

The tide was out. Only in the farness, after the dark yellow-grey sands with the long gleaming streaks of water, the white ruffle of a surfing wave on the grey width of the firth. I decided to walk over to the island.

Silence out there on the sands. Only the sound of rain spitting into the pools, and the occasional cry of a seagull. The big greyness all around. Away to the right, the cranes of Leith; away to the left, the span of the Forth Bridge.

When I got to the island, after all the quiet and the greyness, my attention was held by the ridge of shingle along the tide-line, littered with bright blue mussel-shells.

It seemed a miserable little island, waste and derelict, and I did not know its name. But it was good nevertheless to be walking there. And as I walked further along the path, the bushes and shrubs became more compact, and there was even a woodland, whereas at the point of arrival there was only coarse grass and a ruckle of stones.

I walked among the trees and bushes, and every now and then a bird would whirr in the silence, leaving a trembling twig with rain drops scattered from the leaves.

Then there was a bright-yellow gorse bush. And further on, here and there in the wet tangled greenness, small clumps of bluebells.

I went to the other edge of the island, where the grey sea came surfing in against the rocks, and watched where all around it swirled with thin white surfings shorewards. There was no seeing Fife, the other shore of the firth, only the greyness, and a lighthouse there.

When I got back to Cramond, it was well after five o'clock. There was a strong smell of coal-smoke clinging to the village. The tide was coming in fast.

2

Just along from where I live, lived Velvet Coat, which is the name Robert Louis Stevenson liked to assume when he left respectable Heriot Row and, long-haired and velvet-coated, went damnably bohemian:

> Oh fine religious decent folk
> In virtues flaunting gold and scarlet
> I sneer between two puffs of smoke
> Give me the publican and harlet!

—seeking out crepuscular and crapulous realities among the howffs of the Calton Hill, or the sailor's dens and kitchens down Leith Walk.

It's Saturday night, raining, and I'm out for a walk, passing here in Heriot Row

The Home of
Robert Louis Stevenson
1857-1880

with the lines of tall, goldfish-bowl street lamps strung elegantly along the two pavements, moving on into Abercromby Place, where the *Scots Greys Memorial Club* emits sounds of revelry by night, and further along, past a *Royal Artillery Club*, and a *Masonic Hall*, to Albany Street and the *Hall of the Rechabites* ('Oldest, Largest, Wealthiest'), and further on still to the Forth Street Corner with the *Church of the Nazarene* still loud with an old poster depicting a Man and a Whisky Bottle connected by a Chain and the Bible between them, sundering their evil connection. And then, near enough the church to make it humorous (for in Scotland there is a trinity of Whisky-Religion and Sweets) there is a sweet manufacturers, advertising:

Boilings and Toffees
Pandrops
and
Lozenges

But now we're in Leith Walk, which is one of the 'Glaswegian' or Hyde parts of this Jekyll and Hyde city.

Full moon in the sky. The smell of chips and beer. A disagreement at a corner—'A'll fuchin boot yer mooth in.' The further you go down Leith Walk, especially on a Saturday night, the more language diminishes, various intonations of 'fuck' adequately satisfying the needs of communication, until, when you get right down to Leith, it's only the sea you hear slowly and disconsolately murmuring 'fuck . . . fuck' on the shore.

But we're not there yet. We're at the *Halfway House Bar*. And the *Boundary Bar*. And the *Scandinavian Lutheran Church* (*Den norske Sjømannskirke*). And further on the smell of the sea's beginning to mingle with the smell of beer.

East Old Dock. West Old Dock.

Along to Newhaven, along the Granton shore road, the rain still falling, the moon swollen, the sea fucking away there in the darkness, to the crowdedness and hazy light of this pub at the sea's edge, this pub full of bric-à-brac culled from sundry and diverse sources: shark skins and shrunken heads, old flags and new flags, exotic curiosities dangling from the roof, in the dull yellow light full of drifting blue smoke, with the gaudy old landlady in a canary-yellow kimono and magazine portraits of breasts and buttocks and cunts pinned to the walls.

Plank it here. Have a jar:

> *O wat ye aught o' Fisher Meg*
> *And how she trow'd the webster, O*
> *She loot me see her carrot cunt*
> *And sell'd it for a labster, O*

> *An' heard ye o' the coat o' arms*
> *The Lyon brought our lady O*
> *The crest was couchant sable cunt*
> *The motto 'ready, ready' O . . .*

An ordinary evening in Leith.

3

If you saunter down the High Street and the Canongate, and turn right, in a matter of minutes you're up and out on the windy hills. I was up there this evening (it's early November now, the trees are bare but for a few tipsy yellow leaves; the houses show up long, gaunt and black under the grey sky; and these last couple of days a tough wind has been blowing, carrying rain and ice and the occasional white flash of a snowflake.) It was still light when I climbed up the Mound from Princes Street, stopping at a bookshop for a quick reconnaissance, but as I went down the Canongate the sky, from grey, took on a dark purple colour, with the spires and gables of the city outlined black and stark against it.

Very curious are the closes and the courts of the High Street and the Canongate. Anchor Close there, where the howff of the *Merry Muses of Caledonia* was situated (whisky, smoke, pen and paper for baudy creations, and raucous voices, Rab Burns above them all):

> *Green grow the rashes, O*
> *Green grow the rashes, O*
> *The lasses they hae wimble bores*
> *The widows they hae gashes, O*

and where the first *Encyclopedia Brittanica*, under austere auspices and after much laborious compiling, was printed—a strange (antisyzygical—is that how you spell it?) combination and juxtaposition. Another pleasantly grotesque neighbourhood is constituted by *World's End Close*, which occupies a site down from a dancehall called *McGoo's*, which stands directly opposite the house of the most undancing fellow in christendom, Maister John Knox himself.

Well, I went down the Canongate, then the High Street (is it for history-hungry tourists it's called the Royal Mile?), and it was dark as John Knox's vision of the future when I got to Holyrood Park and climbed up into the hills. There was a rough wind blowing with rain. And I walked over the hills there with Edinburgh pin-pointed in yellow lights below me, and beyond it the dark firth and the coast of Fife. Walking up there, I was filled with exaltation at being on those heights, above this once life-teeming Edinburgh, sending out saluta-tions to the living poets of the place—to Hyuk MacTaggart, salutations; to Iain McKeg, salutations; to Robert Garrulous, salutations; to Rid Biddy McKay, salutations—and with bits of old poetry driving gustily through my brain as if blown there by the wind, driving through there vigorously, blackly, pungently:

Auld Reikie! thou'rt the canty hole
A bield for mony a caldrife soul,
Who snugly at thine ingle loll,
            Baith warm and couth
While roun they gar the bicker roll
            To weet their mouth

which of course is Robert Fergusson (*The Daft Days*). Again, Dunbar (*The Dance of the Sevin Deidly Synnis*):

Than cryd Mahoun for a haleand padyane;
Syne ran a feynd to feche Makfadyane,
Far northwart in a nuke;
But he the correnoch had done schout,
Erschemen so gadderit him abowt,
In Hell grit rowne they tuke.
Thae tarmegantis, wi tag an tatter,
Full lowd in Ersch begowth to clatter,
An rowp lyk revin an ruke:
The devill sa devit wes wi their yell,
That in the depest pot o hell
He smorit thame wi smuke.

Fergusson, Dunbar—but not forgetting the Sculemaister from Dunfermeling, Mister Robert Henryson, and that great beginning to his *Testament of Cresseid*:

Ane doolie sessoun to ane cairfull dyte
Suld correspond, and be equivalent,
Richt sa it wes quhen I began to wryte
This tragedie, the wedder richt fervent
Quhen Aries in middis of the Lent
Schouris of haill can fra the North discend
That scantlie fra the cauld I micht defend.

4

A word or two (how to avoid it) on the Glasgow-Edinburgh dialectic:

If, according to the old song, there's something the matter with Glasgow, for it goes round and round, there's damn little the matter with Edinburgh, for, apart from some few pockets of circular cosmo-hilarious activity (as down Leith way, or at times in Rose Street of the predestined name), Edinburgh stands stock still, and has been so since its last fling in the eighteenth century.

To put it in another way: if Glasgow is an old whore that would like to be loved, and is full of life enough to be lovable, despite some surface characteristics that tend to the repulsive (to put it mildly), Edinburgh is a well-preserved (*preserved*) stuck-up bitch that says: admire me, or else.

It must have been a West Coast man, in revolt against this rigidity and snootiness (Glasgow breeds radicals, while Edinburgh breeds bridge-players—I exaggerate, I exaggerate, but there's no fun in talking about the Glasgow-Edinburgh nexus unless you exaggerate) who made up the rhyme we used to say as kids in Ayrshire:

> *Edinburgh Castle stands on a rock*
> *And every time you pass by, you must show your cock*

The only morally safe place, by the way (Edinburgh's a helluva moral place), to put these verses into practice, is the WC at the corner of Princes Street Gardens, just opposite the National Gallery, a delightful little convenience (as they say), interior-decorated in tasteful mauve paint and tiling, which is the Festival City's answer to Glasgow's huge underworld of an antediluvian lavvy in Central station. Which, again, points out another distinction between the two cities (for a city can be judged by its water-closets, culture, as Nietzsche says, being manifested in all aspects of civic life): the capital is, or would be, intellectual-artistic, whereas Glasgow is mythical.

If Edinburgh is Athens, Glasgow is China. Edinburgh is formal, Glasgow is grotesque. Edinburgh is apollonian, Glasgow is dionysiac. Edinburgh prides itself on its admirable architecture, Glasgow is rank with what James Joyce called 'monstrous marvellosity'. And so on.

Carlyle, who lived a good part of his young years in Edinburgh, before he became the prophet of Craigenputtock and, with the help of Ralph Waldo Emerson, invented American literature, described the city as: 'this accursed, stinking, reeking mass of stones and lime and dung.' That's not how we tend to see Edinburgh today—though it's how we might well describe Glasgow. Edinburgh is not so much, nowadays, a reeking mass, as: form. And when I say form, I mean, of course, New Town—but the form that attracts me most is not that of Georgian architecture, but the kind of thing you see in Huntly House in the Canongate, or Andrew Lamb's House down at Leith. There is stone-mass strictly (and yet freely) held in shape (a curious, lively shape), and I love it. There's something in that late sixteenth, early seventeenth-century architecture which, for me, is of the essence. Glasgow, I think, has nothing like it. If Edinburgh, at its best, means a conscious ordering of energies, the big gallo-western sprawling chaos of a rain-drenched, grimy and greasy metropolis is a subconscious running riot. A man from the east coast where, in general, things are neater (and narrower) once regretted that the west coast had all the imagination and wished that the eastern seaboard might get an infusion of this volatile stuff. Then he reflected that it was perhaps safer to leave things as they were. What exactly, he thought, had the Gaels, those so imaginative tribes, done with the old Scots city of Glasgow? What indeed? A big waste, a bloody mess, a hideous chaos—right. The 'id' of western civilization. No wonder that, after seeing it and living in it for a while, Gerard Manley Hopkins was convinced that there was something badly wrong with the Western world. As for Blake, it's been said he'd have thrown away his bow of burning gold and agreed to call it a day.

We better leave it at that for the moment.

5

It was a chill afternoon in April when I went to Greyfriars Churchyard to visit the tomb of Duncan MacIntyre, or Donnacha ban nan Orain, that is, White Duncan of the Songs, the gaelic bard who was born in Glenorchy and died at Edinburgh in 1812, of whom MacDiarmid writes:

> . . . *only in* your *poetry can we feel we stand*
> *Some snowy November evening under the birch-trees*
> *By a tributary burn that flows*
> *Into the remote and lovely Dundonnell river*
> *And receive the most intimate, most initiating experience*

It's an obelisk that was raised to MacIntyre, decorated with emblems of fighting and hunting (for Duncan of the Songs was a gamekeeper before he enrolled in the Edinburgh City Guard), inscribed on one panel with the words:

> *A few admirers of his genius*
> *have erected*
> *this monument*
> *to denote the last resting place of*
> *Duncan ban MacIntyre*
> *the celebrated Gaelic Bard*

and on another with the elegy MacIntyre wrote for himself:

> *marbh raun an ugudair dha fein*
> *fhir tha d sheasamh air mo lic*
> *bha misa mar tha thu n drest . . .*

On the ledge of the stone, the only stone in the graveyard so adorned, was a bunch of daffodils. Which reminded me of a haiku by Buson, *suisen ya samuki miyako no koko-kashiko*:

Daffodils
here and there
in the cold capital

My next stop was the graveyard of St Cuthbert's, at the tip of Princes Street Gardens, and the gravestone therein of Thomas de Quincey. During his last years, de Quincey would roam the nocturnal streets of Edinburgh, a congenial labyrinth, lost in his dreams that took in misty sphinxes, Manchester fog, Welsh roads, a little Whitechapel prostitute, poppy juice, murderers, seas of faces and, in general, the burden of the Incommunicable. He had rooms rented all over the old town, transcendental rat-holes he would use for working in, cramming them with papers, dossiers, books; till they became 'snowed-up' as he put it, at which moment he'd close the door behind him and look for another place. When he died, there were several such rooms still rented in his name:

Thomas de Quincey
who was born at Greenhay
near Manchester
August 15th 1785
and died in Edinburgh
December 5th 1859

After that little necropolitan exercise, I walk down to Rose Street where I nick into a pub for a glass of whisky, because it's very chill weather indeed, with a thin, bitter wind scything up the melancholy streets. It's lugubrious enough in the pub too: a lofty-roofed Victorian place it is, with antiseptic tiles on the walls to make the surroundings as uncouthy as possible, and only a tired gas fire to afford a wheezy and reluctant warmth. I get my whisky and retire with a book into a corner while the bar-lady in sheer boredom heats herself a pie that sends, momentarily, a whiff of hot, greasy air into the general frigidity.

From scenes like these . . .

PART II

THE GATES

The great path has no gates
When you go through the gateless gate
You walk freely between heaven and earth.
                                    Mumonkan

THE BLUE GATES OF
JANUARY

*Qui d'entre nous ne rêve de forcer les portes du
royaume mystique?*

Georges Bataille

I

They say it rains four days out of three in Brittany, which
doesn't leave a lot of time for anything else. Well, maybe I'm
just lucky at the moment, but it's the middle of January, and
the sky is gloriously blue. The sky's blue, my coat's blue, my
shirt's blue, my franciscan blue-jeans are blue, and there's a
blue flame glowing brightly in my idiot's brain. I'm a blue
devil—and the sun is perched on my shoulder, laughing like
hell.

Travelling this way, where am I going?—nowhere. I pass
through many places of the mind—to get nowhere. Nowhere is
difficult, but I'll get there some day. . . Nowhere is anywhere,
is mywhere.

Who am I?—just a sign for the infinite; maybe a zero.

And, writing this, this way, what am I? A writer, a poet, a
literary (all tied up in the literary nexus) person?—no. I'm not
writing poems, or books (all that gangrenous literature). I'm
just writing a few strong sheaves for the Book, a few chapters
maybe of the coming Bible. I'm part of an answer maybe to a
question that hasn't yet been formulated, that can be formulated
only by a madman, and maybe that madness hasn't been invented
yet.

Hallelujah!

2

Saturday night at Nantes, on the Quai de la Fosse. Soiled girdle of the goddess. Putanas on the way down and out. '*Le commerce baisse.*' Wine heads, pickled pricks, and cheesy cunts. Drink beer in the *Bar de Londres* and dream of lovely Syphilis Abortion, the queen of the balls.

Next morning, Sunday, on the road to Quimperlé.

La Roche-Bernard.

Vannes.

Auray.

Lorient. All the tramps of the vicinity gathering here at the harbour, earning a coin or two unloading fish.

Then, after six hours holy hitch-hiking—Quimperlé.

3

Baudelaire talks of 'means of multiplying the individuality', of 'augmenting personality', of an 'intellectual paradise', of 'a paradisal state of the mind and senses', of 'angelic excitation', of 'immaterial voluptuousness', of obtaining the 'objectivity peculiar to pantheistic poets. . .'

He speaks too of the Scythians, the Sons of the Wind, gathering hemp seeds and scattering them on red-hot stones for an ecstatic vapour-bath. . .

I'll try that bath some time, a super-sauna with intellectual projections, and all of Baudelaire's phrases talk straight to my heart.

But I'll still continue to travel a step at a time, believing that the 'paradise' comes out of the most ordinary reality, and out of 'normal' states. Less spectacular maybe, but more lasting; less intense, but with a greater density.

Gather and control the energy (wakened by movement) of the complete being (the full psychic spectrum), and place it in the midst of naked elements ('nature'), and from there on, I think, you're really on to something substantial. . .

I'm writing you this in Quimperlé, in a little café opposite two buildings: one, the ruins of Colomban, two, a cinema called Eden. I want more than the cinema—looking maybe for a stone, a flower, a key, among the ruins.

(Letter to an acquaintance of Paris and London)

4

Leaving Quimperlé on this chill blue January morning, white frost on the fields, my breath steaming—'now I know my nostrils are turned towards the earth!'

Pont-Aven:

Bonjour, monsieur Gauguin:
'*D'ou venons-nous . . . ou allons-nous?*'

Down on the Quai Théodore Botrel. An old woman washing clothes in the river, a pile of steaming linen beside her on the stones.

Quraak, quraak of gulls. Gulls fat, white, swift. Never fixed, always in flight. Dancing the pantomine of pure desire.

Then into the little *Café de la Régie*—smell of dark, polished wood; fire burning—where I slowly drink a sweet and bitter-black coffee before moving up out of Pont-Aven on the road to Concarneau.

I arrive there (hitch-hiked with an ex-cabin-boy who had done ten hard years on the Dakar run), at midday, coming along the docks with gulls (small pure-white fellows with red beaks, and big brown-flecked black-beaks) clamouring crazily all over the place, and fish being dried in the hangars. Welter, clamour, smell of sea and oil and the fat gleaming sliminess, the glut, blood and fleshiness of the fish. Here I am at home!

Over to the *ville close* in the midday silence. *Tempus fugit velut umbra*—on a sun-dial at the gate. Old folks' home. Two old men muttering Breton on the ramparts.

Along to the edge of town, to the Quai de la Croix and the lighthouse, then back, and out towards Quimper.

5

From Renan (*The Poetry of the Celtic Races*): 'Their mythology is nothing more than a transparent naturalism'; 'the cult of nature . . . of landscape'; 'that impulse of imagination'; 'the principle of the marvel is in nature herself, in her hidden forces, in her inexhaustible fecundity'; 'an unlimited faith in the possible'; 'the Scots . . . doing duty, until the twelfth century, as instructors in grammar and literature to all the west'; 'studious philologists and daring philosophers'; 'perhaps the profoundest instinct of the Celtic people is their desire to penetrate the unknown'; 'we are far from believing that this race has said its last word . . . who knows what it would produce in the domain of intellect, if it hardened itself to an entrance into the world, and subjected its rich and profound nature to the conditions of modern thought? It appears to me that there would result from this combination productions of high originality, a subtle and discreet manner of taking life . . .'

That could be a programme.

6

Rue de Rosmadec:

White walls and gulls
extremity
impossible blackness
rapacious solitude
the narrow garden of joyance.

7

By eleven o'clock the next day, a clear, blustery morning, I'm in
Pont l'Abbé, with three old women, two of them limping, in
bigouden costume (black dress and white lace tunnel-bonnet),
going to market on the Place de la Republique.

Then, away out beyond Penmarc'h (after hitch-hiking with a
girl who talks with pride of her people, the fisher-folk round
Penmarc'h—'*nous sommes particuliers ici*,' '*nous avons peur de rien*'—
and dismisses Quimper as '*bourgeois*'), nothing but rocks, the
wind, and the clamour-shriek of gulls.

It was out here by Penmarc'h (meaning the Horse's Head)
that the crazy Breton poet Tristan Corbière imagined his
Casino des Trépassés, a 'winter station', where he'd bring
together Homer, Dr Faust, Rabelais, Jean Bart, Saint Antoine,
Job, and other '*anciens vivants*', there to live the 'high wild
life' (*la haute vie sauvage*) between the wilderness and the
sea . . ..

I go along to the beach of Pors Carn and, sheltering beside
a rock, out of the cold wind, eat some bread and cheese, then
come   back   into   St Guénolé   and   a   harbour   full   of
multicoloured,   fish-smelling,   weather-beaten,   wave-ridden
boats:

> *La Chaumière du Pêcheur*
> *Men-hir*
> *La Petite Jacqueline*
> *Fils de l'Océan*
> *L'Etoile Filante*
> *Mousse-Bihan-Coz*
> *Koroller ar Mor*
> *Flibustier*
> *Cinq Frères Ademo*
> *Ketty et Micau* . . .

On the shore-road between St Guénolé and the Eckmühl lighthouse, two men and a woman are loading a cart with dark-red wrack.

8

I spent that night in Audierne (walking in the cold evening on the Quai Thézac, with the moon scudding through cloud and the red harbour light shining at the limit), and next morning, very low down the morning, after drinking coffee to waken me and some milk to keep the whiteness in my teeth, I got on the road, making for the extreme point of the Pointe du Raz. A chill morning, overcast, with streaks of dawn redness raw in the sky. Along the road, gorse, fern, heather, and boulders. When, finally, after one or two short lifts, I arrived out at the Pointe, the rain was beginning to come down with a vengeance. I passed by the huddle of tourist shops and cafés now, at this season, all apparently closed and dismal, and passed too the ponderous monument raised 'in gratitude for Catholic help during the sardine crisis of 1903', and walked and clambered out over the boulders, right to the extreme tip, where I sheltered from the now torrential rain under an overhanging rock, with the sea turmoiling viciously green and white below me, gulls keeping up a perpetual caterwauling, and cormorants roosting silent, black, and solitary.

9

grack

rudd

assilsh

shoo and shaa
radgrack

shoo

yaler
radgrack

shaaaaaaaa

10

As I sat out there under my rock smoking a cigarette, a bedraggled starling came to visit me, and then a butterfly, looked like a red admiral—and I wondered what the hell a butterfly was doing out there at that time of year, especially as it fluttered away *seawards*.

So I sat out there for an hour, maybe more, then came back to the little ghost town of tourist shops, where I found one café open, and went in to drink a cup of hot something, discovering at the same time there was a bus leaving in half an hour's time for Douarnenez. I decided to take it, and sat there in the café, with the rain battering against the big, sea-filled windows, and slithering fatly down them, waiting till it came.

'*Hé, vous avez un client!*'—and I'm rolling out in the omnibus on the way to Douarnenez.

Down to the harbour:

> *La Belle Garce*
> *Astarté . . .*

piles of blue and green nets on the railings, blue and green dreamy clouds of nets, and the rain still falling. I go into a *crêperie* for a bite to eat (a *crêpe* with egg, and a *crêpe* with cheese, washed down with cider).

I didn't take any dessert (say, a *crêpe* with honey) with my meal in Douarnenez. My dessert, though I didn't know it then, was on bramble bushes lining the road to Locronan. It's about five miles from Douarnenez to Locronan, and I saunter along them, eating brambles here and there, passing men in farms bagging spuds, and in fields a family howking dark-rosy-red beets[1] from the heavy, wet, rain-soaked, darkly-juiced earth.

---

[1] 'The Blue Gates' condense the material of two Breton journeys, the one made in January, the other (hence the brambles, spuds, and beets) in

In Locronan, then (perfect little town of brown granite, with the story of an Irish saint sculpted in coloured detail on its church's pulpit), as evening's coming on, I take the bus for Camaret, arriving there in pitch, oily darkness (after the yellow light of the bus), and finding myself a room in the annexe of a hotel (along the road, up the steps by the public showers, then to the right along a path), a desolate-looking house, with a wildered garden (one palm tree in the waste like a decadent poet), overlooking the harbour, where I put on the heater (I'm in room o, room Zero) and then go back to the hotel for a meal and a jar of wine before getting out to stroll about the streets of the town in the thick-hanging mussel-blue night.

11

In Camaret, I'm thinking of the poet Saint-Pol-Roux (a Provençal, but who opted for the Breton milieu)—'Saint-Pol-Roux the Magnificent,' whom André Breton called the 'master of images,' and who lived here in Camaret for years, becoming as well-known there as the proverbial White Wolf:

> *The Universe is a quiet catastrophe; the poet . . . searches for what is scarcely breathing under the ruins and brings it to the surface of life.*
>
> *Every being during his life is the centre of Eternity.*
>
> *Poetry must augment its own Eden.*
>
> *The poet is a prodigious explorer of the Absolute.*
>
> *Poetry's becoming bourgeoisified in ordinary gestures.*
>
> *Widen the circle.*

November. Wang Wei (eighth century) in his paintings also mixed the seasons, painting, for example, banana trees under snow, to the great scandal of the critics. The road to the intellectual paradise, we might say, is paved with paradox.

12

Next morning, early on, after dreaming of myriad red herrings, I'm walking along the harbour to the little chapel of Roc'h-a-ma-dour (The Rock amid the Waters), the air thick with the stench of fish, past lines of black hulks in various stages of skeletonisation (which, I learn later, the *Beaux-Arts* maintain there as a treat for the eyes), when I come across the *Saint-Pol-Roux* (number CM 3092), one of the many boats reposing in harbour, waiting to leave again for the fishing grounds off Ireland, or Portugal or Morocco—on the hunt for crayfish (green, red and rosy), lobsters, crabs, spider-crabs, scallops, mackerel, or tunny-fish—travelling the grounds and swells of the sea for these living 'images'.

I stand out at the end of the breakwater (there's something very fishy about the sky this morning—a pale golden light shining, also silver and blue). Then I come back into town to a café for some breakfast—a jug of coffee and a pile of hot butter-cakes, which I wade into with relish, leaving crumbs all over the place.

13

Gaya gaya gaya ka gaya ka gaya gaya gaya gaya gaya gaya ka ka ka gaya ka—keeya! keeya! keeya!—ka ka ka ka gaya kaa kaa gaya gaya gaya gaya . . .

Two silver gulls with pulsing breasts, beaks raised to the heavens, yelling on the gable of a whitewashed house, as I come along the harbour-front at Camaret and climb up out of the town by the Street of the Four Winds.

14

The hazards of hitch-hiking take me down that morning, along the lovely, misty coast, to Châteaulin, then up to Le Faou, from there into Brest (with its little hell of a military port which you look down into from a hideous bridge, its once-hot Rue de Siam, and its long, long, long Rue Jean Jaurès), out of Brest where I wait in its dooly suburbs of Tourbian-Coataudon, whence a car at last takes me in the late and murky afternoon to Landernau, so that finally, with evening coming on fast, I arrive at Huelgoat where, after falling in love at first sight with this grey little granite town, I decide to stay two days, mainly for its woods.

15

In the woods, a blue and gold morning. Beech, oak, and pine—a great coloured, trembling ecstasy. Smoky sunlight. Sound of waters. The rich chack-chack of a blackie. Red leaves of the beech thick on the earth.

Wood-silence, big fertility, gloriousness. Great rounded boulders. Rich water-sound of life flowing deep in the silence. And grotesque, sap-filled roots heaving up out of the pungent earth.

Five hours in the woods.[2]

Then back into them in the evening.

Red ground. Night gathering. Watching the lovely madness of the river, the water coming blackly pulsing and purling in the slits and holes among the rocks.

16

It was in the woods of Huelgoat that the poet Victor Segalen (born in Brest) died, in 1919, after wanderings that took him to

---

[2] There was a path there that particularly attracted me. I later found it described in Senancour's *Obermann*: 'There's a path I like to follow; it describes a circle like the forest itself ... it seems to have no end; it goes through everything and arrives at nothing; I think I could walk this path all my life.'

China and Tibet, on a solitary quest for what he began by calling 'the last pagan' and which he understood finally as a state of sensuous and spiritual plenitude to which he gave no fixed name (except, perhaps, '*le Milieu*': the central kingdom).

'China,' writes Pierre Jean-Jouve, 'was for him the projection of his psychic life, of his ghosts, his erotic ardour, with the deep, very deep call of a spiritual reality.'

What interests me about Segalen is that he seems to epitomize exactly ambitions and desires which, though I'd have difficulty in defining the term, seem peculiarly 'celtic': the search for 'pagan' living, and the search for a spiritual 'China'.

Segalen, travelling through the yellow lands, along the Blue River, into the Empire of himself . . ..

17

At Morlaix, on the Saturday morning, I'm in the town museum, strolling around there in the musty silence, when I come across, in a dark corner and unlabelled, what I'd vaguely hoped to find: a portrait of Tristan Corbière—there he is in his boat, the grotesque face with the long pipe, with a red cap on the head, and red jersey on body, against the dark green of sea and the rough whiteness of the sail where the weird profile of the face appears as blue. A crude, but expressive little picture—like Corbière's poems, those acrid, smoky, harsh, poignant, delirious, terrific, coarse, tragic, comic, brain-storming, soul-tearing texts that made at least one Parisian writer say of him he 'talked nigger'. He talked nigger, all right. He talked hottentot.

A very strange bugger, who gave himself the romantic name of Tristan by derision and, to underline the derision, bestowed the name also on his dog, a beshitten little tike of the most mongrellish origins—a gargoylish figure there in the ports of Brittany, up to crazy doings with his cutter, *Le Négrier*, purposely waiting for the worst weather to go out in it and court there death, maybe his only love. 'Outside the human

track,' as he describes himself, 'a wild poet with a lead pellet in
his wing.'

Tristan, *salut*.

20

And it's on then up to St Pol de Léon and Roscoff, the land of
the Onion Johnnies—Roscoff sleeping its sleep of granite in the
sun when I get there about one in the afternoon and eat my
bread and cheese on the harbour wall before walking further
along the shore and coming on

> *rumpled here at the sea's edge*
> *on the bright blue shingle*
> *pile of marine flesh*
> *colour of wet salt*
> *mushroom-backed with a long*
> *blabber of entrails*

a lovely, big sea-delivered jellyfish and, in the clarity of the
afternoon sun, before the sea, writing my coastal signature,
which closes this little blue notebook of Brittany, so:

$$K \quad \begin{matrix} W & W & W & W \\ W & W & W & W \\ W & W & W & W \\ W & W & W & W \\ W & W & W & W \\ W & W & W & W \end{matrix}$$

P. S. Roscoff, evening, low tide:

> *The sea bares her thighs:*
> *mud weed and crab-humps*
> *blue-lipped molluscs*
> *and the redness of the sun.*

LETTER FROM
AMSTERDAM

*Fellow traveller, I write you a poem in
Amsterdam in the cosmos*

Allen Ginsberg

I

The *Gare du Nord* was the first foreign station I knew, and as I
was leaving it that morning, about ten years after I'd first set
foot in it, I had the feeling of a recapitulation, of having come
full circle, of having come to the end of something, and maybe
the beginning of something else. It was vague, and it was
because I felt this vagueness that I'd decided, pretty well on the
spur of the moment, to make another little trip—this time up to
Amsterdam, just to get out of the melting-pot, to see what I
would discover on the streets of another city, some kind of sign
perhaps.

There were a few other people in the compartment with me:
three Parisian hippies, *Bill, l'Abbé* and *Etoile Filante* (they had
their hip-names painted on the backs of their army-surplus
jackets), making for the *Paradiso*; a German girl, studying
psychology in Amsterdam, with a little dog she called
Woodstock; and an American soldier on leave who, like he was
needing a piss, 'just couldn't wait' (as he said to a Belgian boy
who came in at Brussels). Later on, a Surinamese came in, and
sat staring darkly out the window at the rain.

2

After getting myself a hotel room in the quarter of the Oude
Kerk, I found myself, like everybody else whose intentions on

going to Amsterdam are vague, walking up the Dam Rak, past
the American Express with young Americans offering for sale
anything from a Volkswagen to a pair of shoes, till I came to
Hippie Square, with its horde of vague-eyed wanderers sitting
on the steps of the national monument, waiting for the end, or
the beginning, sitting mostly in stolid silence, though the odd
guitar strumming—like a tribal group when its shaman dies,
showing signs of unrest, distracted, unable to work, sleeping a
lot, talking in their dreams, fleeing individually into the tundra.
Well, I'd been like that too, and maybe still was like that a bit,
but I was no longer of the tribe, and wasn't waiting for another
shaman. I'd maybe just gone a bit further out into the tundra
than my companions, and was concerned with my own dance
there. The 'underground', as they called it, was so full of phoney
shamans (and every shaman is at least part-phoney), that it was
better to be entirely out on your own—better, and harder.

3

So I walked round the Dam, and up to the Spui, where I went
into a smoky little howff for a drink. It was there I met Jaap
Kroll, a musician, mawkit-drunk, who told me that earlier that
year he'd been in New York and in 42nd Street he'd come across
this place where you could put a penny in a slot and see a sex-
film, and he'd gone in there—'bekoss I am innerested *alzo* in
pornograffy'—but what had delighted him was not the sex-films
themselves, but the noises. After taking a peep or two, he'd just
stood in a corner listening ecstatically to all the sexy moans and
groans coming from the boxes, and that had given him the idea
for his new work, *Fuck Symphony No. 42*, on which he was now
working. All he had to do, and it was really combining work
with pleasure, in a big way, was record in his room the
utterances of the women he fucked ('the other night, I haff a
new sound produced . . .'), and then work them up kosmically
on his electronic equipment. With luck, he would fuck it to a

finish by the end of the year, and get it performed in Amsterdam. I said I'd look forward to hearing it. He said to come out to his workshop in Haarlem and hear what he'd already done. I said I might at that.

When I got out on to the street again, it was dark, and I went back down towards the Old Kirk, past all the little crimson-lit hole-in-the-wall bordellos:

'*Hé, motje nog een ritje?*'

—hey, would you like a little ride?

But that night I was happy enough as a pedestrian.

4

I'd sat in my hotel room for a while, glad to be completely alone with my silence, then, feeling hungry, I went out into the streets again, looking for a tavern where I could get a bite to eat.

I found a good place eventually, and sat in the smoky heat listening to a Dutchman half-seas over telling his life story, in Dutch, to two Turkish 'guest workers' who didn't understand a word he was saying but gave an occasional nod and smile to show they were friendly disposed. '*Duitsers zeggen tegen ons,*' said the Dutchman, '*jullie zijn verdomde kaaskoppen.*' The Germans tell us we're damned cheeseheads, but, he went on, they're just '*klootzakken*', bags of balls, and he looked round the room as though to say: 'so there!' A man must live, he continued, a man must live, drink up! But the two Turks made signs they had to be going, and made for the door. 'Take care of yourselves!' cried the Dutchman, and relapsed into a murmured interior monologue, in which I could just make out the words 'old prick' (*ouwe lul*) and 'the cholera' (*de klere*). Then he beamed at the company, said 'Good night,' and staggered out himself. I ordered another glass of *jenever*, thinking of Rip van Winkle . . . When I finally made it out myself, a few *jenevers* later, there was a big full-circled moon sailing grandly over Amsterdam and I felt strangely at home.

5

Next morning in the Rijksmuseum, having asked my way to the
Asian Art section and followed a whole maze of rooms, past
furniture and dolls' houses and crockery and God knows what
all else (they seem to have hidden Asia away in the far-away
basement, lining the way with futilities), I cross yet another
threshold and come up against a big bronze of Shiva Nataraja,
the Lord of the Dance, four-armed Shiva in a dance posture
within a circle of flames, signifying the five-fold action of
Creation, Conservation, Destruction, Incarnation and Deliver-
ance.

This is my kind of God!

I hadn't expected to come smack up against the most central
and profound religious symbol I know. I'm no longer in
Amsterdam, in the Netherlands, I'm at the centre of the cosmos
and Shiva is dancing in me, and the drum is beating, away, way
back to the oldest India, the oldest ground, to Mohenjo-Daro,
and the little naked dancing-girl with the wide-open cunt is
dancing also, past literature and art, past psychology: drum,
cunt, and the transcendental dance. This is what is still in us,
back, back, away back beyond memory. It isn't Shiva I've come
across, it's myself. Filled with the shak-power, aware, deeply
aware, of the dance, the absolute and subtle dance. All I've ever
wanted to do is create a certain space (space out myself), so the
dance can occur, the fundamental encounter, the touching of
the original substance, the elemental integration . . ..

6

That night in my hotel room (I'd bought a newspaper with the
photo of an Indian woman in it and I'd cut out the photo and
pinned it to the wall of my room), I write:

Rain and the Pariah Woman

It's raining
it's been eight weeks long dark raining
and I've been sitting in this empty room
listening to the rain
it's a Europe of rain
(all the bullshit of Europe
washed away in the rain)
and if I speak of Europe
it's because I'm thinking of India
looking at a photograph
cut from a newspaper
pinned to my wall:
the photo of a woman
an Indian woman
a pariah woman
her dark (very dark) face
lit by a smile
a very naked smile—
the WHITE LAUGHTER of Shiva!

I spend a long time with the photo, the poem, and the rain.

7

I'd come across two hippie-boats (barges on which wanderers could lodge) moored in the Amstel, called *Exodus* and *Orpheus*, and the names seemed appropriate to me. *Exodus* for the big secession, and the wandering in the desert; *Orpheus* for the descent into the underworld in search of lost being. But I felt there should be a third boat, and wondered what its name should be. Dionysus? Buddha? Shiva? I'd seen another similar boat, it was true, the boat belonging to *The Lowlands Weed Company*, 'offering you hemp seeds and plants that will grow the purest quality of marijuana', but it seemed to me rather an adjunct of the *Orpheus* boat than another stage. There really should be a third boat—after the exodism (allied to exotism), after the orphism (music and wandering and undergrounding), there had to be something else, but I couldn't define what, and I couldn't think of a satisfactory name for that third conjectured boat.

Exodus, Orpheus—then what?

8

Next morning, I'm sitting quietly in a little coffee-house in the old Jordaan district, then I go out into the Haarlemmer Straat, the rain is still falling, and it's there, as I'm walking along with nothing in my mind (except the vague idea of a rain raga) I smell a faint smell of jasmine, and I'm standing in front of an Indian shop, and I go in, and at first there's no one there and I'm standing alone among the many-coloured shirts and saris, with the smell of smoke-perfume stronger in my nostrils, when this young Indian girl appears from the backshop, dressed in a blue sari, long black hair, red circle on forehead, large round ear-rings, marvellously beautiful. The same blue sari as I saw at fleeting moments in Glasgow, and even in Edinburgh, and in Paris, a kind of star in my night, the same Blue Sari. I'd just have liked to sit there and contemplate her, be with her, not even hold her slender brown wrist, not immediately anyway, just look at her moving about, in her quiet young beauty, but I don't say that because other people, noisy characters, have come into the shop, so I ask her for a box of perfume-sticks ('made of indigenous raw materials', as I see later), jasmine perfume-sticks, and I go back out into the street and the rain, with the sensation of jasmine perfume, slenderness, darkness, her body, her smiling, the blue sari, her hidden nakedness and that all as I walk on under the rain gathers into a feeling of joy, sheer joy, pure unadulterated joy.

I go back to my room, rain falling over the window, dark sky, my mind whole and concentrated, and I light the stick of indigenous raw material and watch the blue smoke dancing fragrantly in the emptiness.

9

Kroll's workshop, Haarlem. When I arrive there in the late afternoon, he's got company: a girl friend, a woman painter, a classical scholar, a professor of literature and a poet. Kroll himself with a coloured bandanna round his cranium, stoned out of his mind. He gives me a smoke, so I can get in tune with the others. The poet talks about 'the hemping of Dutch culture.' Kroll puts on his fuck-music, and does a crazy lurching to it in the middle of the floor. He tells me in a rush that the poet is from the Freezian Islands and that his nickname is Iceberg; that the professor of literature is a Structuralist, with a difference, not like the damned Parisians; that the woman painter is working on orgiastic abstracts inspired by his fuck-music; and that the classical scholar had come to speak with him about Spinoza, because Spinoza was the only philosopher he'd ever thought he might be able to read, because Spinoza wrote music. The classical scholar told me that he'd studied in the States and that he'd been to see Pound recently, which got us on to Ezra. As for Spinoza, they hadn't got round to him yet. They had been talking about the Kabbal. The Kabbal! That started me off about the Shekinah, the meeting which communicates the power of opening the gates of the spiritual world (I was thinking of Blue Sari). The Shekinah, often associated with the sense of smell (Aaron's rod had the perfume of the Shekinah on it)—I was thinking of the jasmine. The Shekinah, I said, was that thing, or notion, or power called the Eternal Feminine. '*Das ewig Weibliche zieht uns hinan.*' quoted the professor of literature. Yes, I said, the Eternal lovely Feminine, and I told him (I was wound up and rarin' to go) of the labyrinthine fogs of Glasgow, and the Blue Sari, and the grim frozenness of Edinburgh, and the Blue Sari, and the funny confusions of Paris, and the Blue

Sari, and how I'd met it again just yesterday, and how I felt I didn't care about anything else any more, just the Blue Sari, that was maybe some innermost essence of myself, and that I was full of it, and that from that moment on I was going to be living in a kind of Blue Sari India. '*Passage to India*,' said the classical scholar (this guy could quote till the cows come home). Yes, I said, and the woman painter started talking (everybody was making crazy connections) about the union with reality of the Sufis, the mystic travellers, advancing towards reality, or Reality, which is maybe just a certain sensation of reality, and I said, yes, and for that the best word I'd ever come across, for that sensation of reality, was the sanskrit term *samarasa*, and that's what it was all about—travelling in the fields of chance, and occasional *samarasa*. And the classical scholar said this was maybe what Spinoza was talking about too, what he called the third kind of knowledge, and his philosophy too was a philosophy of joy—'joy is the passage of a man from a lesser to a greater perfection,' he quoted in Latin, and just as he said it, Kroll's cabin, I swear on this book, blew up into the air, right up into the air, and we were all flying about there on wings of cosmic laughter.

Yes.

WINTER ON THE PLAINS

Ce n'est qu'un vaste champ ouvert au déploiement d'une vigueur

Roger Caillois

I

When, in Meudon, I turned on the tap in my room about five in the morning, the water ran thinly, choked with feathery ice that crushed pleasantly in the fingers as I washed.

The station was quiet. Only the huge tick of the yellow-faced clock, a kind of mathematical, sexless moon. There are about twenty people on the platform, even at this early hour in the morning, all with beards and whiskers of frozen breath. A silver express hurtles and screams by, sending a tide of hoar-frost rushing along the platform.

Smell of soap in the train. That's the morning smell. At night it's sweat.

At Montparnasse-Bienvenue I take the métro line to the Gare de l'Est. Métro line in the morning. Two passengers out of three have their eyes closed. Most of them are ugly: that drunk there with the dead thatch of hair, the scarred, bloated face and the dirty fawn overcoat; the *agent de police* there, burly and brutal, with his cape hooked round his truncheon and a black woollen scarf round his neck. . .

I get out at the Gare de l'Est. Big heap of the station there, with the trains howling. But I have time. So I go for a breakfast—to one of those big cafés where the light is yellow and acrid as vinegar.

There is buttered bread piled up on plates on the counter. I'll have a couple of these and a coffee. I sit down. A child is wa-

waaling somewhere. My neighbour drinks black coffee and reads the *Parisien* with a surly expression on his face.

2

In the train, the long green train for Châlons-sur-Marne and then away out into the khaki grounds of the east.

Hordes of soldiers on the train, making for Nancy.

Carriage full of the noise of farts, chops moving, and the raking of throats and noses. I'm longing for the open country, longing to get out of Paris, into clear spaces.

I look up at the high walls of Paris as we pull out along the line.

7:40. It's still dark. Waiting for the dawn.

3

Epernay, with its green river and smoke stacks, the river frozen white in its narrower reaches.

As we rush along, I see sudden flashes of whiteness in the woods. Patches of snow still lying.

Saw the sun just outside Châlons, already a good way up the sky, apricot-coloured, clear-defined, sailing through cloud. Had it in view for about ten minutes, then it paled, quince-coloured for a last moment, and plunged away.

4

Open country:

> *The cry now is for a wide-open poem*
> *a poem plain but curving with power*
> *set bare on reality, a january poem*
> *for whiteness and the winter of ecstasy.*

Lonely on fields of sand and salt, birds
wheeling in wild flight, walking through woods
where streams are frozen round birches
the sun sailing through cloud, burnt-yellow
seen and unseen in swift-running cloud
moving on soil virgin and desolate . . .

5

Writing this in an open field—Paris no longer exists—in the lee of a pile of straw bales. Patches of snow still on this straw. I've made myself a resting-place in out of the keen wind. The sun's a mass of sparkling whiteness, the sky blue with cloud like the first seizure of ice on water. Twittering and chittering of birds, their leaping lunging flight. A bell ringing far away at the level-crossing. Trees look so complete with their bare branches and twigs you wonder what they ever do with foliage. The straw's rustling all around me in the wind and my writing hand is growing numb with cold. Let's move.

6

Just moving. The sheer sweep of the land, peppery-brown and pungent.

Walk another while, then sit down at the base of a fir tree. Little fir copse at the side of the road.

But must keep moving. Can't stop for long. It's too cold.

7

A circle of peppery fields, some closely harrowed, others with the stubble still on them and round the stubble a thin frost haze. I'm in the centre of these fields now, that radiate away from me over the horizon, with birds chittering all around me and further off the lazy black flap of a crow. A goods-train passes on the

line through the fields, smoke belching from its funnel in thick
white curdles then greying and disappearing.

8

Hawthorn tree. Crabbed and spiky. Green-yellow lichen on its
branches. At its base, husks of berries left over from a bird feast.

9

Steaming lines of dung on the fields. Mounds of beets encased in
earth and straw—at places they've been eaten into and the beets
appear red and sore, glistening, chapped by the frost.

10

Birch wood: glistening, slender strength. Saw it suddenly,
gleaming there, glistering, with a halo of frost above it.

11

Near village now, here at the graveyard. Before the yard, a tree
with great clumps of mistletoe hanging from its branches, the
berries gleaming.
    I go down into the village. Hens and duck. The stream frozen.
A red tractor there in a farmyard. Four men on a massive pile
of dung—hot and steaming, the dung in the frosty air—forking
the stuff on to a cart.

12

This cold is killing the seed. The snow is good, brings down
the azote from the air, and is a fertiliser. But this cold is deadly.
    It is minus 17 degrees here in Champagne. In the Vercors,
thirty below. The road to Spain is blocked, and all the canals of
eastern France have frozen over.

I went down to the cellar and chopped wood all morning.

13

Went along the river—icy green, the river, still flowing, the banks ruffed with ice. Where trees bowed branches down to the river and where twigs touched the water, ice had formed, ragged white patches of ice on the green water surface and at the tip of the twigs, like blossom.

Today in the plains area of France the temperature is 20 below. But in the wood on the other side of the river, it was quite warm. A sun of distant gold was shining, glinting in the frosty haze around the trees and on the clumps of mistletoe on every hand. It breaks easily, the mistletoe, its twigs being hardly made of wood, but of a kind of fleshiness which fastens on the tree-bark and drinks in the sap. Saw many other berries, crimson and black, with birds frantic among them. There was a hawthorn in particular weighed down with dark-red clusters, a ferocious nourishment and fertility in this frost. Ate a few berries myself.

14

Went out this night along the road that leads southwards out of town. The moon was a yellow sliver in the sky, clutched in a cloud of frost. About a kilometre out, I came to the level-crossing, its twin oil lamps burning. I passed over it. Darkness and silence—save for a little black and white piebald dog which had been strolling around me for some time and which could now be heard rustling in the frosty grass. It unearths a bird that whirrs off into the darkness. A light, and a car comes up behind me, lamps wide, and is forced to slow down for the little dog now trotting in the middle of the road. It comes close to my legs as it has already done once or twice, and I stroke it. Only the two of us in that road, in the darkness.

A train rushes through the fields, a murky orange crest whooming above its engine. Then silence again and darkness. The town has disappeared under the curve of the plain. There is only the dark curve of fields before me, and the frost and moonlit road. As I go on and come nearer the villages (St Etienne, Les Grandes Chapelles, Villette) I hear dogs howling and barking on all sides. When I come to the crossroads, I think it is as good a moment as any to turn back. But before doing so, I stand still, for a long time.

15

Dawn came this morning in a wet mist, visibility about twenty yards. As I looked from my window, the first thing I saw was a row of cabbages, green tousled cabbages, thirty-three of them.

16

The mist lifted during the day, but has come down again now at half-past-five. I went for a walk along the southern road. Quarter moon, yellow in blue. The lamps at the level-crossing reddish, their flame throbbing. Mist and the feeling of distance.

17

In my room, as I was sitting quiet, I heard a fluttering behind me at the window, and looking round saw a butterfly, red, yellow and black, beating its wings at the glass.

Maybe, with this thaw, it thinks that Spring has come already.

It's crawling over the floor now, stops for a few moments with wings spread, then folds them.

I go out for a walk, but when I return, I look for the butterfly, which I find eventually under the bed, with wings closed.

It's not Spring, yet, butterfly, but I hope you'll see it.

Summer Postscript:

I

The railway track out from Châlons-sur-Marne to Troyes is white, its ballast consisting in the chalk stone of the plains. It is lined with patches of fir and pine, grotesque in shape from the wind of the plains. At nine in the morning, in a mist of sunlight, the micheline auto-rail sways along past bare villages and tiny level-crossings, where a woman maybe will have been washing clothes just before closing the gate. You may also see a horse or a tractor moving across fields. But soon all you're left with is the impression of open expanse, austere, unadorned, the plains and the sky.

2

Writing now in Arcis-sur-Aube, a little township lost in the plains, lodged in a clean, uncluttered room, whitewashed and with only a vase containing bulrushes as decoration. The sun is blazing hot, and a dusty, massive heat—as though the sky were threshing—weighs over the countryside. Few people pass on the roadway, and the shutters are half-down on the windows. There is a great silence, and I sit in the half-shadow of the room, my eyes closed, full of burning images. After carrying a heavy weight for a long time, and laying it down, you feel aggrandized and powerful, even in your fatigue. So I feel now, with a soul-weight removed from my life.

3

Evening now, the sky serene, slate-blue in colour, cold and calm. Behind that quietude, thunder rolls, like the voice of the earth, the pounding of its heart. And the sky is illumined with break after break of sheer white light. There is the long green-shadowed plain, with an occasional single tree on the horizon, the sky, the deep thunder, and the lightning. Later, the tension relaxes; the sky opens in the east, where a hanging milky whiteness dazzles, and in the west where the sun throws a claw of crimson against the gathering night. I sit by the window till the last bird ceases to sing. Then I light the lamp on the table. At about midnight, it begins to rain. The window is wide open, and the room is full of the smell of wetness.

4

I have come out into the fields. The sun in the greyish sky is as quiet as a flower. There is a wind blowing, but it is not a heroic wind; it hardly shakes the sturdy green corn, though it causes some commotion in the rye. At the moment I am sitting in a strip of woodland between two fields, and there is a small grey bird tip-toe on a pine-tree branch trembling and squealing for all its worth. All over the green stretch of fields, a whistling of birds.

As I sit here on the stump of a tree, moths are flitting among the grasses, and bees. The wind is growing stronger and is beginning to whoom through the pine tree. I feel the first faint prickle of rain in the air. I cowrie down beside a bush. The grass smells very strong. Close by a yellow snail clings to a stalk; and a pale blue moth, alighted on another, is gyrating slowly.

5

I fell asleep there under the bush. When I awoke, it was to great excitement, both in myself and outside. The rain had ceased and the sun was streaming. A wild rose bush close at hand was noisy with bees. The birds too seemed to be whistling louder. I came out of the woodland and began to walk round and round it, unhurried but intensely. My nostrils were filled with the scents of grasses and flowers. I went round and round that patch of woodland, then I went into it again and lay down among its bushes on the heavy grass.

FLEMISH WEEKEND

*C'est kermesse là-bas et férie au hameau de
Saint-Job*

Michel de Ghelderode

I

Paris was plunged in the smoky redness of a June sunset when
my train pulled out of the gloomy Gare de l'Est. I had my old
torn and battered grey suitcase with me, in which I'd thrown a
change of clothes, and was making for Meaux, where my friend
Christian Vanderloo was to be waiting for me with his car to
take me to his place, an old farmhouse he'd bought just a year
before in the village of Foligny, where he lived with his wife
and three kids. There was an old man from Charleville in the
compartment with me—I knew he was from Charleville, because
he kept asking me if the train was going to Charleville—and I
felt like asking him if he knew the Rimbauds, but I didn't.

Vanderloo was waiting sure enough at the station, and we
drove through the now thick blue night to his house. He'd
painted some of the rooms, but the room in which we ate
dinner was still bare, with a whitewash that had gone grey and
yellow over the years. On one of the walls, in a big way, and in
red he had calligraphed two Chinese characters: *t'ai ch'i* (First
Principle).

2

The idea was that we make a trip to Belgium together to see
some people, friends of his, friends of mine (though I'd never
met them, just corresponded with them). So next morning,
around nine, in clear sunlight, and with the wind shaking hedges
and trees, we were on the road—first stop Louvain, where

Vanderloo teaches the history of Buddhism, and where that afternoon we were to listen to a comrade of his presenting his thesis on the *Samantapasadika*. Vanderloo was also working on a thesis, a translation with notes of a sutra called (OK, take a deep breath) the *Pratyutpannasammuk-havasthita-samadhisutra* ('the sutra of the samadhi in which you get the Buddha to appear before you'), and he wanted to see how things went.

It was good travelling up to the border—the poplars swaying smoothly in the wind, and the June sun fixed in a bright blue sky—laughing our heads off at nothing at all. And then we were over the line, into Belgium. The time to have a meal, and it was Louvain, redbrick and Roman Catholic, the thesis-writer, just back from Japan, with a little blue silk bundle of necessaries (*furoshiki*) before him on the table, nervous as hell and deferent as a man who believes in it all. It dragged on for a couple of hours. The guy got his doctorate.

3

It had been arranged that we'd meet Isenbrandt, a sculptor, and Susie Coecke his lady-friend, who'd both been fellow-students of Chinese at Louvain with Vanderloo, at the thesis-do, and the four of us left the academy together—Isenbrandt to make a bee-line for home where he had a bit of work waiting for him, the other three of us to take it easier and buy in food and drink for the night.

We made for a supermarket, and went through it like the Mongols invading China—weaving up and down the aisles, picking up booty here and there: rice? sure; vegetables, galore; noodles, of course; wine, chocolate, whisky, bread, cake, pork, spices, sauces, bacon, prunes, you name it ... till we had two prams full, loaded them into the car, and brought it all home.

Through Brussels, getting lost in the suburbs: Vilwoorde, Melsbroek, Grimbergen, Wolvertem ... the night ripening fast ... till we get to the village of Rambroeken, and go through it down to the canal to this building beside the lift-bridge with the lights blazing, which is the workshop.

4

It's a huge barn-like room, with a great fireplace, the walls painted a lurid, house-of-Usher red, an antique sturdy fantastically carved table in the centre with two tall silver candlesticks, and all along the walls, bronze sculptures, all on the one theme: dongs and ballocks. Massive bullroarers in bronze, dark glowing bronze, all over the shop. All those heavy genitals hanging from the shadowy pelvis of the world, filling the air with a deep silence, and in this deep, red silence, Tibetan music (*b'dong* ... *b'dong* ... *ksh!*) booming and clashing away from the recordplayer. . . .

While Isenbrandt puts the finishing touches to a wax dummy, Vanderloo and Susie go into the kitchen to get the meal started, and I set about lighting the fire, bringing in wood from the big straggly pile outside, twigs, branches, and logs, till flames are leaping, and unctuous smells are wafting from the kitchen, and Isenbrandt (work put by for the day) is calling for wine and beginning to swing lumberously to his Tibetan jazz.

The fire roars and crackles, the music clashes and booms, the smells of food get thicker and thicker, the cocks and balls glow darker and darker, shadows prance wilder and wilder on the walls, the candles are aglow, the bottles are open, the glasses are full and empty and full, the food is on the table, rice and meat and vegetables, in vast quantities, and we all fall to, hungry and already half-drunk.

5

In the middle of the meal, the door bell (a big bell, like the one Frère Jacques was supposed to ring Matins with) rang, and it was an architect and his wife who were clients of Isenbrandt's.

At this point, I became solipsistic, because everybody, who'd been speaking French before, started speaking Flemish, and my notions of Flemish don't rise to architecture or whatever, so I went off into a little reverie on my own—about the mad Fleming Hieronymus Bosch, his gargoylian visions, his medieval devilry, his hellish horrific humour, and his strange, subtle quietness . . . which meditation was interrupted an hour or so later when the clients left taking a couple of hundred quids' worth of bronze genitals with them.

6

It was then, close on midnight, that the two Dutchmen came in: Pieter and Joachim, who help Isenbrandt to cast his bronze. It was Friday night, and they'd been out on a spree—now returned with about thirty glasses of strong Belgian beer each behind them in their long trail along the dark canal.

Woops!—they weren't too steady on their pins, at least Joachim wasn't. He had long black hair and the face of a mystic ascetic: something like the Ancient Mariner. Pieter was a sight for sore eyes too, with his blond hair and beard, his copper-rimmed glasses, his red shirt, covered as he was in a fine, white dust as though he'd just taken a quiet crawl through a flour mill.

I took to these two right away.

'*Yum, yum, yum, yum,*' said Pieter as he sat down at the table while Susie served him with food and put a fork in his groping hand. While the same was being done for Joachim, pale as death, gleaming-eyed, he kept staring at me and said something in Dutch. Pieter, who knew a little English, translated.

'He says you have a mind, and you know how to touch it.'

While Joachim after that million-dollar remark retreated into silence, I got into talk with Pieter.

He told me he'd been to Scotland once. In Edinburgh. He'd got off the boat at Leith, and couldn't find his way back to it, lost in the Edinburgh streets. He'd stopped two or three people asking them: 'Tell me the way to heaven, please,' but they didn't seem to catch on. Probably thought he was off his nut. He thought they were all off their nut. All he was asking them for was the way to the *haven*, the harbour (they looked like he was asking them something weird, wonderful, and probably wicked). It was only two years later when he knew a bit more English that the mystery cleared.

He also told me he was saving up to go to Japan—to get tattooed.

7

Snooping around the room while everybody was busy talking, Joachim had discovered a bottle of whisky and was swallowing it down lustily as though it were Vichy water. Before he conked out definitively, I went over to have a friendly go at him with the couple of Dutch phrases I retain from a month's intensive study with Assimil. He thrust the bottle of whisky at me. I took a drink, and handed him the bottle back: '*Dank u,*' I said, '*De grote, rode Boot is op de Kanaal!*' My informing him that the big, red boat was on the canal seemed to delight him (maybe it reached him as a remark of esoteric significance), and I was just about to go on to tell him that the baker in this street makes tarts and cookies (and that one would certainly have blown his mind) when somebody suggested we all go out on the canal.

'*Geweldig!*' said Pieter, which I take to mean 'great!'—so we all went out on to the canal, Joachim included, drunker than Li Po, under the moon.

8

There was an old iron canal boat fastened by a chain to a ring on the canal-side near the bridge. After some ineffectual chugging at the chain by sundry hands, Isenbrandt went back to his workshop and reappeared with a couple of pairs of pliers with which he prised open one of the links in the chain, so that the boat was ours to do with what we liked.

The trouble was that on one side our way was cut off by a big, fat barge that took up all the room, and on the other by the lift-bridge, too lowset for the boat to pass under, so that all we could do was go symbolically round and round or to and fro in the small space at our disposal, paddling with shovels (which Isenbrandt had also resourcefully produced from his workshop).

Tiring of the sport this afforded, Vanderloo and Pieter and Isenbrandt started climbing monkey-wise up and along the lift-bridge, while Joachim started to take off his clothes and wanted to jump in the canal, dissuaded only at the last minute by Susie who caught him by the hair, and I knelt up at the prow of the old canal boat till we all decided we'd had enough, fixed up the boat chain again, and went back into the house, where the conversation drifted around for a while, got lost in murky creeks, and sleep began to seem a good idea.

Pieter and Joachim (Pieter on Joachim's back—he'd gone back to the whisky-bottle and dropped into a solid coma) left for the house they lived in on the other side of the canal, and the rest of us went to the sleeping quarters upstairs.

It was close on dawn.

9

At one point there was a ladder, and I climbed up the ladder into an egg, and the egg burst, and I fell into the canal . . .. At another, there was a red bagpipe in the sky blowing furiously over Brussels . . ..

10

Next morning, after breakfast with lots of coffee, while Vanderloo took a run into Brussels on business, I walked along the green waters of the canal, its banks thick with wild iris and weeds, and then went over the lift-bridge to the house of Pieter and Joachim, where they were busy, up to the eyes in plaster, making moulds for future casting.

Quiet, the June sun at the window, and the work going on. A girl went by on a bike along the path. Joachim said something. '*Me kloten*,' said Pieter ('balls').

There were bits of bronze sculpture on a table. One, a nude girl, a dancer maybe, about a foot long. I picked it up, admiring it. Pieter came over, telling me how as bronze it was a failure, but fingering the smooth belly, saying in French (which he was learning): '*C'est le trop meilleur.*'

Then a nun went by on the path, like a two-wheeled bat, and Joachim made some comment to which Pieter answered: '*me kloten*,' which seemed to be a habit with him.

And the work went on, surely, quietly.

11

At dinner, there was talk of art-communes (we'd all get together and live happily ever after), then Vanderloo and I left for Bruges where his parents lived.

Lovely, quiet Bruges.

I promised myself I'd spend a week of winter up there some time, in some clean, simple room—away from all fuss, dust and noise.

Yes, I'd spend a cool week up there.

In Bruges of the canals and quiet courtyards.

12

It was already late afternoon when we left Bruges, making for Ghlin, in the Hainaut industrial belt.

Along the road, red sky, scarred fields, here and there the metal and smoke of a factory.

When we got to Ghlin, the town was quiet, the streets empty. We asked at a *bistrot* for the street we were looking for, finally got to it, dark, with small red-stone one-storeyed houses lining it, found the door we wanted, rang.

It was Marc came to the door. I hadn't seen him in three years—since he'd made the trip up to Scotland to see me. He'd come off a fishing-smack at Fairlie Pier, asked where I lived, and been directed to my parents' home. He was sitting there having a meal when I got a phone-call (I was living in Edinburgh at the time) from my sister, who'd run out to the phone-booth on the corner, to tell me that this character, a Belgian, had turned up out of nowhere, with a beard, a big rucksack, and about ten words of English. She wanted to know if they were to send him on to me. I said yes.

So they put him on the train for Glasgow, and told him to change trains there for Edinburgh, where he arrived about three hours later. He'd been on the road for about ten days.

He attracted a lot of attention in Edinburgh. Long-haired and straggle-bearded, with that rucksack (he had volumes of Fulcanelli and Ouspenski in it), and a tall, thick stave, he made a little sensation in the Calvinistic coffee-house we went to next morning to talk.

He finally stayed in Edinburgh a fortnight, and we spent the time walking and talking, from Princes Street to Leith, from the Calton Hill to Arthur's Seat, and from Thomas the Rhymer to Ruysbroek passing through Whitman and Henry Thoreau. . . .

And now here he was again, clean-shaven this time, looking younger though he was three years older, and I was glad to see him. We took each other by the shoulders and embraced. 'We've been waiting for you,' he said.

Behind him was Marthe, the 'mother' of the group, with eyes like anemones and emotion written all over her.

I introduced Vanderloo, and we went into the living-room, where he and I were introduced to Jacques, Marthe's husband, and the three children, and Max, a poet, and his wife, and Marc's girl. That made quite a little crowd in there.

The table was ready set, and we sat down at it right away, to eat, drink, and talk: a feast of union.

Four hours later, we were still at it. Max, who had been going steady at the wine, was now speaking up about death, rosy death. Writing for him wasn't communication, it was already a 'being beyond'. When he came home from the bank where he worked, he'd shut himself up hermetically in his room, drink wine, smoke oriental cigarettes, and write his (strangely nineteenth-century) poetry. His wife, who was eight months pregnant, said he was too much absorbed in himself, he should quit that job in the bank, and he'd be less obsessed by death. Maybe she was right. Anyway, having solemnly made his statement, Max sank back into himself.

Meanwhile, the table cleared, the general conversation (revolution, communities, writers, books, drugs, children, education, Buddhism) went on, and then became more mobile— till at one point Marthe dramatically took the centre of the room and, gesticulating with her cigarette in the air, half-sobbing, her eyes full of tears, her body one quivering flame, made a long, incoherent speech in which she said it was fortunate that I existed, that she had faith in me, that I would pretend not to understand what she was getting at, yes. I would just sit there watching her 'making a fool of herself. . . '.

To cool the atmosphere, I suggested a walk under the stars.

13

Four in the morning, and I was talking in a corner with Jacques and Marc. Vanderloo was talking in another part of the room with Marthe and Max's wife. Max himself was in a dwam, and Marc's girl was sleeping in animal beauty on the floor . . .

Then somebody suggested another walk. This time we took the cars—Vanderloo and myself, Marthe, Jacques, and Marc— and made for a wood in the vicinity, a fine substantial beech wood over which dawn was just beginning to break.

We walked through the wood (I was desperate now for a

little silence), among the beeches and the holly-bushes, and dawn grew in the sky, and it was chilly there in the wood, especially as we'd had no sleep, but had talked, and talked, and talked.

We all lay sprawled on the grass for a while, half-sleeping, half-watching the rising sun and the dew on the spiders' webs, but it was too cold for comfort, so we went back to the house, and everybody drifted off to bed, closing the curtains to keep out the Sunday daylight.

14

After coffee and rolls in the early afternoon, Marc and his girl and Marthe accompanied Vanderloo and me into Mons, to visit the town before heading back for France.

It was meant to be a quiet stroll of about an hour or so, but we ended up in a café with round after round of beer talking our heads off again.

It was late on in the afternoon before we finally got on the homeward road.

I spent that night at Vanderloo's place, delving in his Chinese and Sanskrit bookshelves, and next morning took a train from Meaux back into Paris, with books in my suitcase and a little Flemish flame in my brain.

GRASS IN THE STREETS OF ANTWERP

Ça se passe à Anvers
Prévert

Une ville très port de mer
Max Elskamp

I

I blew into Antwerp on the back of a hurricane, at a cool 120 miles an hour. Don't know where it came from, hell-holes of Iceland maybe, had turned the North Sea upside down, bruised Britain, skimmed Scandinavia, whoomed over Holland. That's where I'd met it, just outside Dordrecht, coming down from Amsterdam—wires down along the line, so the train had to shunt back to Dordrecht, where we had to take a bus to a doll's house village, from there another train to Roosendael, where we finally made the through train for Brussels. This all allowed me to make the acquaintance of Poepke, a bank clerk who does the exchange service on the train between Dordrecht and Roosendael and can say 'Do you want to change money' in thirty languages including Eskimo (you never know) and Welsh. Also Else, who works as a freelance interpreter in Brussels of the intergnashional organisations. But it was the wind that got closest to me. And there it was in Antwerp when I got off the train that night, ripping TV aerials off the cowering roofs, splintering all glass in sight and in general having a randy time. The newspapers (I saw 'em in the morning) were already at their machines pounding out headlines on it. *'Grote Stormschade in onze Gewesten,'* said the *Gazet van Antwerpen.* '*Noordwester geselde ons Land,'* said *Het Volk.* '*Orkaan raast over ons Land,'* said *De Telegraaf.* And so on. *Chaos in Verkeer! Catastrofe in Westland!*

The wind blew me through the dark and shuttered streets. Blew me down to St Jacob's Market, along the Kipdorp, to St Paulusstraat, where I saw this one-eyed place offering lodgings, with special conditions for travellers, so I barged in, bringing a few miles of hurricane with me, and there was a room, way up on the sixth floor, up the narrow staircase lugubrious, and I open the door and fall into the bed, and, yes, it'll do. A print of *Rosa centifolia foliacea* on the wall, and the shit-house on the landing full of shit (plumber got lost in the gale). A little smoke, the hundred-petalled rose, and so to sleep.

2

A raw blue morning:

> *The rumbling of lorries*
> *along innumerable quais*
>
> *Bataviastraat, Montevideostraat*
>
> *the sun's an eternally*
> *uncut diamond*
>
> *while the* Nove Anna *from Copenhagen*
> *unloads tomato juice*
>
> *Maria José counts her cash*
> *in the* Caribbean Bar

3

There was the copper-haired beauty of Brabant, watching Lohengrin's boat coming wagnerianly up the Escaut. And there was the hedonist communist from Old Zeland, Tanchelin. And Eloi the Slater, who had no big ideas—the big dumb ideas that turn the machinery of history—but just wanted to enjoy his life,

and encourage others to enjoy theirs. All in the Chronicles of
Antwerp, *Semini God!* And weren't the skippers of the river a
wild lot of anarchistic kerls who didn't suffer authority gladly?
And wasn't the place rank with *klompdragers* and *turlupins* and
homines intelligentiae? And didn't Thomas the More publish his
Utopia from here? So if you ask me why the devil I should
come to Antwerp, without having raw diamonds in my pocket,
there you have your answer, *Semini God*—apart from the mere
drifting here and there that does without a reason.

So it's Waalsekaai and Vlaamsekaai, Van Dijckkaai and
Jordaenskaai, Brouwersvliet and Ankerrui, Paardenmarkt and
Keapdorp, Melkmarkt and Eiermarkt, Vlemindkveld and
Schoytestraat. . ..

Hour after windy blue hour.

4

A freshly extroverted Englishman with a wee beard and big
glasses is waltzing round in gay abandon.

'*Le beau Julien*' is at the counter, starched collar turned up,
starched cuffs wide open, a drunken Byron, and flanking him
are his two cronies, a thin and long-nosed character who might
be a reincarnation of Villon, and a leather-coated, stoutish,
middle-aged gent straight from a Simenon novel. There is also
Willy, a pixilated old loon with grey flax round his poll who
wanders around from beer to beer rubbing his hands and
muttering dark secrets. And at the table next to mine sits a boyo
with a bloody bandage round his fist and in it a mug of beer,
sullen, sullen. The rest is noisy background, conversation, music,
tinkling of cash. We're in the café called *De Muze*.

> *Oh to be in England*
> *now that April's there*

sings the liberated Englishman. 'Ah, Spring,' he continues,
hyper-lyrically, 'sweet lovely Spring.'

Julien looks up glowering: 'Spring is a crying window!' he shouts.

The Englishman opens his mouth in mock wonder, and nods his head in exaggerated appreciation:

'That's an interesting line,' he says, 'but it's only one line.'

'I am a one-line man,' says Julien magnificently, straightening up and towering over the little Englishman:

'Do you like two-line men?'

'I like women,' titters the Englishman. Then he says to Long-Nose:

'Is he a poet?'

'He is a lion,' says Long-Nose. 'He will eat you.'

'Oh, not now please,' says the Englishman, 'I don't taste good at this time of night.'

Pause all round. Julien is back to his beer. Long-Nose glares crazily at the Englishman.

'You look drunk,' says the Englishman to Long-Nose.

'You look stupid,' says Long-Nose.

'Let's have some music,' says the resourceful Englishman, and he waltzes over to the juke-box, takes a coin out of his pocket with a flourish, and sets the thing going:

'I wanna be elected . . .' sings a voice. Julien looks up from his beer:

'I *am* elected!' he roars.

5

Cold outside, the gale still hugely enjoying itself, no one in the streets to ask the way, and I want to get to another place called *De Engel*. I hoof it for a while in the blustery dark, getting nowhere, then I see someone coming towards me on the pavement, young fellow, all muffled up. I stop him, ask him how to get to the *Engel*. He's silent for a moment, then he says:

'I'll show you. I can't explain. *Je suis stoned. Je suis presque toujours stoned.*'

'What on?' I ask, as we go down a sidestreet.
'Shitraal,' he says.
'What's that,' I say.
'A mixture of Nepal and Afghanistan,' he says.
'Good?' I say.
'Not bad,' he says.
'Try this,' I say, and offer him some of my noola grass.
. . .
'Where are you from?' he says.
'Paris,' I say.
'*Alors, tu es Parisien,*' he says.
'That's right,' I say.
'*Moi, je suis Anversois,*' he says, '*Antwerpenaar.*'
'What's it like in Antwerp?' I say.
'Stoned,' he says, and laughs.
. . .
'That's *De Engel,*' he says.
'How about a drink?' I say.
'*D'accord,*' he says.

6

In the time of the great quiet drifting, and the age of the *aurora borealis.* Lodged in a decomposing city, Master Unckebunck plays a blue-toned clarinet. Soul to soul. Jefferson climbs into his aeroplane, Credence looks for clear water. Under the red flag, raise the purifying wind. This is real shit, paint a masterpiece with it. High-high Joe gone to Mexico, composing bad poems. That crystal skull. The solution. Earth diamond. It's not what it means, it's what it does—but it's also what it means. In a country devoid of negativist dialectic, there's always the madman. Sweet madmen in clod-hopping England. Kit, Will and Joe. The French dawn-men: Breton, Artaud, Bataille, Char—and Valéry. Cosmic signs. Not so long ago, that Spring sky, the wisp-drift of white cloud, and a rainbow circling the

incandescent sun. Perfect. Cool euphoria. White world. Quiet.
Naked girl quiet. The red dakini danced out. The golden
Egyptian girl swimming. Yellow body adored. Brown, red,
yellow, white, brown, yellow, red. Cosmos. To make cosmos.
Earth diamond. The solution out of the dissolution. Art is a
hazardous dance. Break your neck. Wandering. Dark streets,
blue mountains. Rooms and islands. Clouds of poetry, he
thought, clouds of poetry, but where's the lightning? Aesthetics
of light. Erigena. The Arabs. A medieval ghost in the Rue St
Victor, saw it, shining, while flics gathered like bats around the
Mutualité. Solidarity of the peoples of Indochina. Yellow body
adored. Under the red flag, the purifying wind. *Il ne faut pas
politiser l'art, il faut artiser la politique.* Synthesis, dancing synthesis. The purifying wind. The cold wind of dawn. Beginnings,
beginnings. Once I lived among pigs, now I live among gulls.
The gull academy. Taoist scholars and poets. Cool, clear,
dancing, laughing men. The minister of war glowers, and brings
up his values in armoured tanks. They executed Hi K'ang. They
chased Brecht. They—the undrifting, the undancing. Who do
not know the dialectic. The mono-men. Reducing the space of
living. So the Romantics went into the Gobi desert of the mind.
If you tie subtle movements to less subtle movements (even if
you approve of 'em), which themselves are . . . the very subtle
is going to get lost in the crush, so it all has to go on at different
levels. The lotus grows in its own space. Master Unckebunck
understands. Master Unckebunck smokes the noola grass and
understands. Who are *you?* asked the caterpillar. The modern
poet—a fisherman in winter. The Eskimo smelled out the lie of
the land. Do you know the story of the Eskimo who went to
India? That's me. In a kayak. In a kayak with no name. Here's
to Eloi, Eloi of Antwerp.

7

Next morning I'm on the train to Paris. Two Moroccans in the compartment, on leave from Dutch factories, going home; an American girl with a rucksack reading *The Scientific Analysis of Personality* (now what would that have to say about Master Unckebunck?); and a man (he turns out to be a South African from Jo'burg) reading an English newspaper. This gives me a chance to catch up on the news. The Soviets have made a move against the Buryat Buddhists and against women wearing trousers; and Mohammed Ali has been nominated for the Chair of Poetry at Oxford . . .. So everything's fine. I go to sleep.

A few kilometres from the French border, the customs come on the train. I'm asked to open my case. The man rummages in it:

'What's that?' He holds up a package.

'A book.'

'Unwrap it, *s'il vous plaît.*'

He takes it, looks at it, sniffs it, flips through its pages. Then he says to the plain-clothes police-fellow who's come up behind and is quizzing the two Moroccans (*'Où est ta maison, ta casbah?'*):

'I've got a book here.'

'Bon, je vais voir ça.'

He finishes grilling the Moroccans, then comes for the book, asking for my papers. I give him my *carte de séjour*. He looks through my card, then examines the book, flipping through its pages like the other, coming back to the title, which was:

> *Psycho-cosmical Evolution*
> *by Prof. Konrad Unckebunck*
> *with the research assistance of*
> *I. M. Shitraal*

'De quoi ça parle?' he says.

'The expanding universe,' I say, 'from a psychic and a physical point of view.'

'Where did you buy it?'

'In Amsterdam.'

'Why did you buy it in Amsterdam?'

'Because that's where I came across it. I buy books all over the place.'

He considers my statements, then looks again at the book, putting two and two together and getting Suspicion.

'*Vous allez descendre à la prochaine gare,*' he says.

'Why?' I say.

'*Je vous expliquerai plus tard,*' he says, and disappears with the book and my card. Meanwhile the customs man has been rummaging on faithfully inside my case, uncapping a toothpaste tube, trying to twist the heels off my spare pair of shoes pawing everything in sight. He's looking for marijuana heroin and all hell's pharmacopeia, and he damned well isn't finding it. If you're wondering where my noola grass is, it's invisible. At last the customs man leaves my case alone and makes for the South African. He's tapping dutifully at the man's tape-recorder when the police-fellow comes back.

'*Ça va,*' he says to the customs-man, and gives him my book and card, saying nothing to me. He must have gone to consult his secret list of badman books, and Professor Unckebunck wasn't on it. Which was very cunning of Professor Unckebunk, and very lucky for me.

In the familiar Paris underground again, making for my lodgings, I find myself singing:

Now Sinbad was in bad
in London and in Rome
in bad in Trinidad
and twice as bad at home. . .

Where in hell did *that* come from???

AS A BREAKING WAVE

*She will plunge into the house and there will be
light in the body.*

Kanha

I

That Spring, I was wandering about in the south, around Arles,
on the Plaine de la Crau, in Les Saintes Maries, and in the
Camargue. Of all the places I'd been through, it was the
Camargue that had attracted me most and left me tense with
expectation.

A land of pools and marshes. Of wind, solitude, and silence.
A land of light, where water becomes light, where the flow
becomes an essence. A nakedness, an austerity, a monotony, an
abstraction. A clump of reeds shaken in the wind; an angry blue
squall of rain rushing across the sun; white sand rivuletted by
wind and water; a snake slithering over the mud; the carcass of
a bird half eaten away by the salt, for the salt is everywhere, the
earth is impregnated with it. The Camargue is the hieroglyph of
a stump of branch projecting above the surface of a marsh, or
the ideogram of a shell encrusted in sand. It is the quick
excitement of seeing lithe forms in rippling water and the feeling
that at any moment you may meet that girl, that woman, 'her
smooth legs still bearing the salt of the primal sea'. . ..

2

When I saw her that morning, she was wearing a dark red
poncho. Long, very long black hair. My whole being gave a jolt
when she appeared there on the road, so perfectly southern that
she looked Indian.

She lived in Lyons, but was spending a few days on her own

in a little *calanque* on the coast near Marseilles, where she was born. She had just driven out to the Camargue for the day, and was going back that evening.

We spent the day together, and a good part of the night. It was about five in the morning when we got into Marseilles, and made the twenty minutes drive through the suburbs. Then it was up the chalky crest covered with scrub-oak, grey and dark-green, dawn breaking, the smell of the sea—and down to the *calanque*. A gull's cry out there in the dawn, all of life concentrated in it.

3

We were up about ten. While she made some breakfast, I climbed up the slope to get a bird's eye view of the place. A *calanque* between chalk cliffs, a cluster of cabins, smoke rising blue in the cool morning air, boats in the harbour, two or three fishing smacks. The kind of place I could live in ... I saw her come to the door of the cabin, waved, and went down to her.

While we were eating our bread and coffee, three Swiss, members of a Geneva diving club, passed on their way to breakfast in the café. It appeared they had achieved a monumental *cuite* the night before, with pastis, wine and cognac, and were pleased with themselves. The captain of the team was a little brown-bearded man with a red tartan cap on his head, always telling the others: '*Ne soyez pas si Suisses en quelque sorte!*' ("Don't be so Swiss!"). The big milky-faced one was a travelling salesman in chocolate. Then there was the gendarme, amateur geologist, always picking up stones and enquiring after their identity.

They invited us to a *raclette* in their cabin that evening.

4

We walked out to the cape, along a narrow path among rocks

and shrubs, climbing till we were well above the *calanque* and walking along the skyline, in the openness. Desertic flowers among the rocks, intense concentrations of colour all the more remarkable for their rarity. I am at home in the desertic landscape, with thought concentrated on only one or two signs, concentrated to the point of a kind of madness—'normality' being a state of soft incoherence. Blue-flowered *romarin*. Thyme strong in the nostrils.

Walking there together, on that narrow path, in the openness. With these signs of life around us.

We went right to the extremity of the cape, watching the sea come pounding in against the rock, and the dance of gulls there. Out on the edge, together:

> *like sea-birds on a cliff*

> *always alive to desire*
> *always at the knife-edge of life*

5

At the knife edge. Let there be no talk of love. Let nothing dull the sharpness of the reality. Nothing of the sentimental, nothing of the social. Sudden and absolute, and though tempted to make a halt, keep it that way, pure and unencumbered, pure as a breaking wave ('the hollow curve of a wave about to break,' she'd said), yes, realise the wave.

Thinking all this disjointedly as we came down the narrow path from the headland, then back into the clear country of ten words, seeing the sun reflected on the sea:

> *sun reflected on running waters*
> *a jewel for her nakedness*

6

There was a big crowd in the cabin of the Swiss that evening. A great plate of baked potatoes on the table, and a shining array of bottles of white wine, and Henri the gendarme sweating away at the big fire where he had a massive slab of Swiss cheese resting on a plank with its bared edge to the flame. He holds it to the fire till it is soft and scrapable, then cradles it in his arm and scrapes the softness with a big knife on to a plate, then starts all over again, red-faced and serviceable, dousing the plank with water when it catches fire, making heavy ('don't be so Swiss!') jokes with the Captain who is expounding his Swiss chauvinism (and it's all so noisy and unreal), saying he'd go through the country to the north (i.e. Germany) with a flame thrower, and how much he loathes even to hear the language he calls '*schnock*'.

The cabin's full of heat and smoke, the wine going down rapidly in the bottles, and the Swiss have already moved from wine to schnaps, intending to get '*carbonisés*' again. Getting '*carbonisés*' seems to be their favourite sport, at least on land. Only time they aren't '*carbonisés*' must be when they're underwater.

We leave about eleven—want to sleep under the pines. Go to the cabin to collect sleeping-bags and walk out then along the left branch of the *calanque* till we find a convenient place.

7

Pine, moon, the sound of the sea. We take each other there, under the big wild drifting of the moon and with the curvings and swirlings of the sea out there in the darkness. And when we're quiet again, I'm grateful, to all of creation, to have her there with me, all the beauty of her: hair, jaw-bone, breasts, belly, buttocks, cunt, all the lovely substance of her being, and we lie there together, watching the pine-tops swaying in the little breeze that has sprung up, and the moon veering down the sky in its cloud-drift, till we move again into our own delirium.

8

The cave in the great mountain is deep. There the whole world breaks.

He who knows the jewel of the spirit that flourishes in the Innate, knows the way. Who else knows it, among all the talkers?

He who has stilled his mind by joyance in the Innate, achieves sovereign presence in that very moment.

He who has understood this has understood everything.

If you can put a lock on the gates of the breath, and in the darkness make a lamp of the mind, you reach the ultimate.

It is the best of mountains, the place of the greatest joy.

When the whole earth is gathered into the body, the word and spirit go far.

Just as salt is dissolved in water, so the mind that takes its woman.

9

If I say that what I'm trying to write here, however clumsily, is a metaphysical text, though not as the philosophers, if I even go so far as to say that my meeting with that girl was metaphysical, the pigs, and I don't blame them, will snigger. Trampling under their feet this subtle physics of life, they can hardly have the slightest inkling of meta-physics. Ruysbroeck talks about 'the essential meeting with God in the nakedness of one's being.' That's what I'm trying to get at. The purely physical rising into the metaphysical, beyond the personal nexus. Though I'd never speak of 'God'. My world isn't a God-world. Before, the world was full of God, now it's full of Man, and I'm at home in neither. Both of them are noisy, heavy, and burdensome.

For me, the free play of emptiness-plenitude, and the truth, that is the pure wave—a precarious form, an illuminated nothingness, a power that knows no domination—rising from it.

Truth, as Hegel says somewhere (I used to read so much philosophy) being a delirium in which each of the participants is dissolved ('a woman wants to be foam', she'd said), but which, once this dissolution is complete, is itself simple and transparent.

Simple and transparent.

Almost nothing.

10

On the afternoon of that day, we went to visit the widow of a German who had lived in the *calanque*, making his living as a fisherman, and had been drowned off the Cape five years before.

I noted the books on the shelves: Hesse, Rilke, Nietzsche (one line in the Nietzsche strongly underlined: '*I am alone, and I want to be alone, with the clear sky and the sea*'.)

But what struck me most was a musical instrument, now lodged in the upstairs room, which he had been working at when he died: a stringed instrument, its base a drifted treetrunk. I had never played a musical instrument myself, but for years I had had the *idea* of a musical instrument, *sui generis*, which would play an absolute music.

I would like to have known this man. Also trying to express, by some *unedited* sound, what was deepest in himself.

11

Two days later, I left from the station of St Charles in Marseilles, making for Paris and the north ('You come and go, you come and go, where will all this end?'). It was a beautiful, clear Spring morning, and it was all in her eyes. A line from the Greek anthology came into my head: 'No girl so lovely as you, no girl who ever looked into sunlight,' and I spoke it aloud. On that station platform, beside the train, and a few miles away the sea was dancing, with a thousand sun-crested waves.

NIGHT IN BARCELONA

The effluvium of beauty one receives through the eyes

Plato

I

Spain (and in this of course it's only representative, part of a world with the mangies) has got a gigantic advertising itch, at least on that coast road down to Barcelona. Not only is every farm surrounded by four or five 400 square-footers, huge multi-coloured hoardings advertising anything from whisky to underpants, but they've even got adverts floating in the briny sea. If you go swimming on that part of the Spanish coast, especially, if you're one of those professional-style people that forge ahead with face in the water not looking much where you're going, be careful you don't collide with a yoghurt—yes, there they float, and there they bob, the yoghurt adverts, huge whale-like tubs, exact replicas of the real small thing, and the jocund bathers frolicking and dallying all around them. There's something almost mythological about it. I mean, does this setting of yoghurt right in the middle of nature make people accept it as *part* of nature, the way they accept trees and mountains? When, their holiday over, they rememorise the natural scenes of their joy and freedom, when they see the blue elemental sea coursing in against the ever-virgin shores, do they also see those big tubs bobbing into the picture, and when they say over to themselves the mystic words such as Costa Brava—Sun—Sea—Beach, do they also say Danone, the trade name of this particular product? Are there maybe even poets in the making who will compose odes to Danone the way Tennyson did to Oenone? Will Danone be the new god of the sea? Has Poseidon, that mythical old salt, had it? Is the child now being born who will grow up to think that those tubs have *always* been there, that they are part integral of the sea-landscape and will she wonder maybe (like that kid in Sandburg's poem) what the sun advertises?—in the poem it's the moon, I know.

I came down that road two days ago. I'd been wandering about in the Corbières district (an interesting area, with little vicious ranges of white hills in a Colorado landscape) and I'd decided to come down further and have a look at Spain, by way of the coast. So I went to Perpignan, where you could hardly move for traffic, great circus hordes of it in every square, honking and fuming and apparently getting nowhere, and got a car to take me over the frontier as far as Ampurias. There, after a couple of hours on the beach and strolling around the graeco-roman ruins, the grey walls and the olive trees, the sea-patterned tessellated floors, I slept the night on the sands, and next morning, after a leisurely swim and another walk round the ruins, struck out again on the main road, heading for Barcelona.

I made it finally with two sun-burnt boys from Birmingham in a rattling Ford (they told me it was a Ford, my own technical know-how stops somewhere around the neolithic) that rattled up to a camping-ground just a couple of miles from the city, where we parted company, and I hoofed my way on in on my own (by God, that's a beauty!).

2

The hotel I was in that night was some ancient palace with pillars everywhere, and tarnished mirrors, and brown lighting scarcely penetrating the dusty gloom. I think it was called *El Paraiso*. For sheer worn-out elegance and decrepitude, I'd never seen anything like it.

But there was something better to come. The next morning, I was walking quietly through the streets of Barcelona, minding my own business, when this surrealistic monstrosity howled up in front of me like a nightmare. 'What is it?' I asked a passer-by. 'It is a church,' he said, 'it is the church of Gaudi.' For a moment I thought 'Gaudi' must be a Barcelona nickname for God, so completely had this apparition shattered my nerves, then I remembered about that architect who'd taken it into his head to out-grotesque the grotesque, out-baroque the baroque, out-surrealise the surrealist and build his visceral vision in stone to the glory of the Holy Family who, however much at one time they may have been preoccupied with lodgings, could never in their wildest dreams have imagined this. It out-Danted Dante, it out-Swedenborged Swedenborg, it positively out-Popocatapetled Popocatapetl.

I walked on—'live and go', that's the motto. And ended up around midday at a café near the metro station of Triunfo Norte, where I ordered a beer with *tapas* (first a plate of anchovies, with bread, then, still being hungry, a plate of olives, with more bread) and gazed out upon the world. And what did I see? I saw a van go by bearing an advertisement for a film: *El Hijo de Jesse James*; then I saw a second van go by bearing an advertisement for *Panico en Bangkok*; and pretty soon I saw a third van go by bearing an advertisement for *El Regreso de Fu Manchu*. At this, I began to feel melancholy. The day before it was yoghurt, and now it was Fu Manchu. I felt distinctly melancholy. The beer also was having its effect. Beer always makes me feel melancholy. I began to wonder what I was doing there in Barcelona, why the hell I had come there in the first place, I should have stayed in the Corbières, away from yoghurts and Fu Manchu, and I said to myself, aloud, what Céline wrote about travel: '*ce petit vertige pour couillons,*' but no sooner had I done so than a shoe-shine man who'd settled down a few seats away with his box for a breather, thinking I was addressing him, came up to do business. Now I've never had my shoes shoe-shined in my life, and hadn't intended it this time, but I liked the look of this little Charlie Chaplin man so much I didn't have the heart to say him nay. The only difficulty was, I was wearing those Japanese rubber no-shoes called tongs which, apart from the sole, consist of two thin straps connected at and held by the big toe and the second toe. They are quite unshoe-shinable. But that was a minor difficulty. Before there could be any misunderstanding between us, I delved into my rucksack and pulled out a pair of good shoes which I presented to the shiner, and on which he got immediately to work. He made a marvellous job of it. My shoes were beaming. I thanked him and paid him, he thanked me and pocketed the money, and went off on his business. I left soon after, having put on a pair of socks, wearing the shoes. I felt better for it. There's something in having a good pair of kicks on your feet.

3

By early evening, after having spent most of the afternoon in the area of the harbour, where there was a naval exhibition going on, with modern ships and shiplets moored beside a resplendent *Santa Maria* and where I saw behind a counter in a shop a beautiful young dark lovely girl with whom—God, she was lovely—I tried to talk in Spanish, I found myself in what I now know was the Barrio Gotico, the gothic district, which wholly deserves its name. It's grim. It's religion and history, two depressing subjects (give me metaphysics and geography any day). Long, gaunt, imposing architecture full of gloom, and streets that lead you to an overwhelming question—'Oh, do not ask what is it, let us go and make our visit', as the man said (he always turns up in the most miserable precincts).

Well, I'm wandering round that murky gothic district in the rainy afternoon, and I come into this weird building that is a huge church with chapels built in dark niches all round its walls, and which is at the same time a public square with people crossing it from one street to another, a great dark covered square with a murky yellow light around the altar where a service is going on. It's a real horror of a place this, rank with the smell of piety, and with the signs of piety hanging everywhere on the iron gratings closing off the chapels: waxen arms, waxen legs and hearts tied with string to the bars in grateful remembrance of, or anticipation of, miracles. In one chapel a wedding's going on, in another a baptism—and all the time there's the dark crowd moving through the darkness from one greyness to another. I go outside again where there is a little kind of cloister with colonnades, and a couple of swans floating in a pool of water, a couple of degenerate swans floating about in the dirty water, pale in the darkness of evening coming down among the gruesome gothic stones.

I make my way over to the *ramblas* and ramble there for a while, with the strolling crowd, past the flowers and the books and the café tables, till the night really gets thick. Then I go down into the Barrio Chino, the Chinese quarter. Symbolic journey—out of the nightmare of history into the China of the mind!

4

So I'm down there in the hot, seething little *calles*, with a roasting chicken spurting grease in blue flames in a sooty corner, and light dripping on the painted lips and eyes of queens, fairies and other goblin-like creatures of the night, and the crowd packed in those narrow ways jostling past bodegas and bars (*San Francisco—Texas—Moby Dick*) and where food lies fishy and colourful and smelling on trays, in barrels, in pails, clawing at the air.

'*Yoop-yoop! yoop-yoop!*'—that's an American sailor-boy coming out of a hotel with a catalan whore: '*yoop-yoop! yoop-yoop!*' he cries to the bunch of old wineys in the café. '*Yoop-yoop*,' what is it: an infantile cry of triumph from the great grandson of big chief Brooding Buffalo?—something like that. '*Yoop-yoop!*' America calling. Texas Tim on the rampage.

Three others coming up the *calle*, their arms interlocked, a big one, a medium one, and a little one, in that order, three yankee sailors, blotto, singing:

I got a girl her eyes are green
She goes down like a submarine
Yoo! Yah! Yee!

(the last three sounds proferred by the big one, the medium one, and the little one respectively). America calling again. America calling. '*Me cago en la puta*,' I shit in the pute, says a Spanishman darkly, chewing on a vicious peppercorn.

And then it gets quieter and darker and miserabler, I'm away at the bottom of this street I think's called the Calle San Pablo, away at the dead end of the Calle San Pablo, where there are no longer any women visible, only men humped in sordid drink-shops with pale blue TV screens flickering in the darkness, yes this is the end, with a pale-green-painted little hospital-looking shop there advertising *lavajes-siphilis*, the syphilitic end of the overhuman bloody world.

5

So I retrace my steps, back into the lights and the noise and the spurting of an aliver at least reality. And it's passing in front of a bodega with big windows that I see this woman of dark stunning beauty that stops me deadstill there on the sidewalk, fascinated, staring at her, till she turns round, and a whole table of faces turn round with her, and she gives me a smile that melts the marrow in my bones, and she says, her divine eyes flashing, '*le gusto*,' do you like me, do you want me, and I say '*si*,' and the crowd of faces with eyes like coins drag her away into the noise, drag her away into the hectic noise, while I lurch away into the darkness towards the dark-swirling animalistic waters of eternal eros.

INSULAR DELIRIUM

*We all follow an eccentric path, and there is no
other way possible from childhood to completion.*
Hölderlin

I

The ferry made back to the mainland. Hitching my pack on my
back, I made out on the road up the island. It was raining. The
equinox. Big tides. You could hear the calm force of the green
waves exploding lazily on the beach. The world a grey wet
greenness. I met no one on the road.

Having found myself a hotel room in the island's main town,
I went out again to buy some food. I was being served with
cheese in a grocery when my eye fell on a shelf bearing bottles
of golden whisky, like a symbol of the past. So with the cheese,
and a loaf, I purchased also a bottle of whisky, and thus
provisioned came back up to my room. It was already dark.
From my room I could still hear the sea, pounding away in the
darkness. I ate some bread and cheese, and then uncapped the
whisky-bottle and (riding on the whisky) went back home to the
Skotlandsfirdir.

2 .

goddess
dark wind blowing in from the sea
this dawn
the deepblue mussel-beds
writhe and crackle
the salt sand

> *reflects in its pools*
> > *the awakened gulls*
> *and the first*
> > *redness*
> > > *as you open your belly*
> > > *over the island*
> *and the day comes cold and howling*

3

Next morning, another grey, drizzling day, the horizon silvery, I went down to the shore early on—there were two men with a cart gathering in seaweed—and walked along the edge of the tide for a mile or so, and then came back along the shingle-line picking up shells:

> *Venus ovata*
> *Venus sasina*
> *Venus mercenaria* . . .

I went back to the hotel then, made up my pack, and was on the road again further up the island. I was making for the lighthouse: the Lighthouse of the Whales, at the extreme point.

4

It was a long walk up to the Lighthouse, past the small fields fertilised with wrack, the dunes and the pine trees, the oyster parks and the salt-marshes, and when I got up there, I was the only visitor—the tourist season was over—so the guardian, to save himself the climb, let me go up the tower on my own.

At the top of the stone steps was the guardian's cabin, which I passed through and went up the few remaining steps to the bridge directly under the light. The wind was blowing strong, with grey-white cloud breaking in the sky, a green sea scudding against the shore, a green sea with blue reflections here, pale sandy reflections there, and the whole coastline of the island hazed with spray.

I stood up there for a while, then went back down to the little round, wood-panelled, brass-fitted cabin, whose sole furniture was a bunk fitted into the wall. It had apparently not been used for some time.

The cabin had two windows. It was very silent in there, though you could hear the wind, subdued, outside. . .

I was thinking of other such tower-rooms I'd visited: the tower study at Culross, Yeats' tower at Galway, and Montaigne's tower library: 'It's on the third floor of a tower . . .. In shape it is round, the floor being flat enough just for my table and chair. . . It has three wide, unobstructed views, and is sixteen paces in diameter . . . very windy . . . that it be difficult of access pleases me . . . I try for pure domination there . . .'

5

They call this island (probably because its base is limestone): the white island. This pleases me, as also that it is a place of salt, a place where salt concentrates, a place of concentration.

The search for a place of concentration, that's what my travelling is all about, my writing, the travelling-writing is one indivisible process, because I don't hold much with a thinking from which the body is absent.

The centre is where I space myself out.

6

Yes, what I am aware of in my depths is an energy (which does not very well know what to *make* of itself, and perhaps prefers to remain pure, undefined, energy), pursuing fantastic figures in open space.

7

A chant for childhood:

Birch rites
empty moors
raw skies
incredible snow

mussel beds
gull screams
lost islands
moonglow

wet woods
heron shells
crimson leaves
dark rain

hare pads
lightning flash
written rocks
begin again

8

Sitting on the shingle-line, facing the sea, remembering Baudelaire's: 'In certain, almost supernatural states of mind, the entire depth of life is revealed in the spectacle, however ordinary it may be, which one has under one's eyes,' and Boethius' definition of eternity: 'the presence, all at once, and in measureless intensity, of unending life.'

Plenitude of life. It exists under an apparent stillness, lack of 'interest'. All the occupations and interests with which we concern ourselves, and which are called 'living', are, to someone who knows, or who desires (and to desire is at least to know in part) the plenitude of life, quite beside the *point*, mere diversions, nuisances. They have nothing to do with the deepest desire, the life-desire. In so much of our living, truth, life-truth gets in only by chance, and is quickly stifled, or translated into insignificance (even poetry can be just a kind of wordy deflection).

To maintain desire *in its whole form*—that is my ethos. What do I mean by the 'whole form' of desire?

Desire can be fragmented. It can be reduced to a hundred little satisfactions. Ad nauseam.

Desire in its whole form is indivisible. It is the *intention* of the whole body, the whole being.

9

Thinking now of Archilochus, first of European lyricists, born on Paros (a few fig trees, goats on the rocks) in the Aegean, who wrote of himself: 'I am plunged in desire . . . So violent was the desire that swelled in me like a sea and covered my eyes with mist,' and of a girl: 'like the halcyon on the promontory rock, she would beat her wings and take her flight.'

The always original situation.

10

Last image as darkness begins to come (I've been sitting all afternoon on the shore):

On the point of an anfractuous rock, a sturdy, crazy and determined-looking gannet, swiping the air with its wings, ready to make off somewhere, I wondered where.

THE BIG RAIN AT TIGH GEAL

When I first saw him, he was slightly drunk, and said: "Could you paste this paper on the wall?" Then he rose and made two bamboos, a bare tree, and a strange rock.

Mi Fu, referring to Su Shih

I

The 'white house' of the title is an old Skye cottage which, abandoned for years, was taken over recently by an Irishman from Glasgow, and it was this Irishman from Glasgow, Michael Mulligatawny by name, who invited me here. In Glasgow, Michael is as civilized a solicitor as you'll find between Scotstoun and Camlachie, but here in Skye he goes native, with a big heathen kilt round his hurdies, a Celtic football strip on his back, and boggy wellingtons on his feet. He is 'chust sublime', as one of his favourite characters in literature would put it. Some wee English woman writer avid for local colour is bound to put him into her book one day ('Miss Effie Dudds has written yet another charming account of life in the Western Highlands'). Anyway, Michael took over this cottage which was falling to rack and ruin, and made a good job of putting it together again, adding a few Irish features on the way. There's the half-door, for instance. When he'd finished it, Michael asked his neighbour, Big Donald the postman, what he thought of it, and Big Donald thought of it and then said thoughtfully: 'Oh, it iss a very fine door, Michael, a very fine door indeed—but where iss the horse?' Another Irish feature is an ingenious bellows which Mulligatawny imported from an antique shop in Dublin. It's fixed into the hearth, and you work it by turning a wheel, which puts a fine rambustious flame into the sometimes reluctant peat. There's a fine fire glowing at the moment back of me there. I'm seated at a big table beside the window, and outside the rain is coming down, naturally enough, in buckets. There's the smell of peat in my nostrils and even a little taste of it on my tongue—coming from the bottle of island whisky just a few inches nor-nor-west of my left elbow. Everything is chust sublime. Michael has gone back to Glasgow, leaving me the cottage for ten days, though he tells me there may be some sporadic visits from other island-hungry Glaswegians. Back in Scotland after five years and having travelled about a bit, some kind of a reckoning and an accounting I suppose is called for (you can't just come and go without a cheep), but we won't make it circumstantial, no, we won't make a day's work of it, we'll just let it come as it likes, out of the rain ... 'All our troubles,' as Gogol's madman says, 'stem from the mistaken notion that thoughts originate in the brain, whereas, in fact, thoughts are not born in the brain, no, not at all, they are blown in from somewhere around the Caspian Sea.'

2

Talking about the Caspian Sea (now *there's* a nifty transition), that's probably where we all came from anyway. Before we started moving up the blue Danube (*die schöne blaue Donau*) and along the shores of the Mediterranean, and then fanned out further into the secret mists. I mean those stone-working, stone-obsessed tribes, moving out in successive waves from that original area. I like the etymology of the word Keltoi as 'mountain men'—and if they raised stones elsewhere, it might have been, apart from anything else, to remind themselves of their origins. A big question, origins. The primal concern: gods, ancestors, homelands. And a vexed problem, identity— *who am I*? That's been my *koan*, as it were—the insoluble question. But when you've worked at it long enough, there comes a kind of solution. I've worked at it for a long time, if not long enough. Looking for the real space, the real self. From imaginative extravaganzas concerning Indo-Scythians, steppe-wandering and maybe touching the Indus valley; through contemplation of that yogi-type figure you can see on the Gundestrup Bowl, and on the stone in the museum at Reims: yogic posture, antlered cap, holding—on the bowl at least, an earlier piece—a snake in one hand, and a bracelet in the other, surrounded by animals, as though the aim were an integration into nature; from and through all that to the consideration of closer family alchemies:

> *When I think of them all*
>
> *a dancing rascal*
> *a red-bearded fisherman*
> *a red-flag waver*
> *a red-eyed scholar*
> *a drunken motherfucker*
>
> *I take a look in the mirror*
> *and I wonder . . .*

Scot. I like the etymology of that word as 'wanderer'. Yes, that's it. The extravagant (*extra vagans*: wandering outside) Scot. *Scotus vagans*. Wandering, more or less obscurely, in accordance with a fundamental orientation. Which brings us (going hither and thither, but you get there in the end) to the Orient. I no longer remember when that seed of the East got planted in me, but the soil was ready and it took root, naturally, unobtrusively, without straining or excessive flourish. It went along with that urge, always present, not to be embedded in history, but to work a way out of it. Out of MacNies and Camerons and Mackenzies and MacGregors—the white. A kind of transpersonal thing. A breathing space, a cool area. *Kensho jobutsu*. Seeing into your own nature is becoming Buddha. But what is Buddha? Seeing into your own nature, *entendu*. Listen to that curlew out there.

3

Not knowing where you are, who you are, in order to get into the nowhere, the no-who-where, and let the essential images come. Sitting here fingering a piece of purple coral from a beach a few miles away. Aloneness, with glimpses of grey seal, heron, bog-cotton in the wind. Outside in the greyness, if you listen, listen, in addition to the curlew's ripple, the yelp-yelp of the redshank and the sempiternal *ka-gaya-ka* of the gull. To know how to sink deep into that aloneness.

4

The smell of dawn goes well with porridge ... Sitting at the window, looking out at the dripping rowan tree, and beyond it the misty rain and beyond the rain, though invisible, the mountains and the sea:

Ninnin kono shōen no tokoro ari. Ika naru ka kore nanji ga shōen no tokoro?

Sōshin no hakushuko o kissu; ima ni itatte mata ue o obou.

Everyone has his own native place. Where is your native place?

Early morning I ate rice gruel; now I feel hungry again.

5

Coming into Glasgow again. The mauve evening thickening into purple above the orange-lighted streets. A drunk bleeding in a close. A woman's voice on Exchange Square: 'She had a bad time wi yon bastard.' Late final, late final. The old room:

On the first wall
was a print of Hokusai
on the second
was an X-ray photo of my ribs
on the third
was a long quotation from Nietzsche
on the fourth
was nothing at all

that's the wall I went through
before I arrived here

But the old haunts of the thaumaturgic errancies no longer there.
Charing Cross blasted by motorways. Is the White Tower still
there down by the Tollcross? I didn't go to see. I didn't go
over to the Gorbals either. 'They're destroyin' the image of
Glasgow.' The old stinking bog out of which, potentially, the
lotus could grow. But nothing can grow in money. Offices and
hotels. A place defined only by cash. Let Glasgow flourish,
b'jees—the damned place is booming (big deal, big deal), but not
blooming (two or three tubfuls of geraniums thrown to the
pedestrians don't mean a thing). The future, a flyover.
Remember St Enoch's? Remember? Remember? Remember? No
use going over to Crown Street, nobody there any more. A
sterile, desiccated purgatory (no wonder the seven-day licence
has such significance):

A went tae a party wan Friday nite
The Tongs wur there an' wantit tae fite
A drew ma blade oot quick as a flash
An' shoutit 'Young Team, young Team, Ya Bass'
The first wan that came wis five foot four
A liftit ma boot an' he fell tae the floor

The cunt wis in agony, the cunt wis in pain
So a liftit ma boot an' a fuckt him again.[3]

Even the eyes of the Pakistani girls don't seem so much 'like silver fish' as they did in the city's old murky ocean.

6

Went out, the rain still falling, for a walk along the shore:

A grey shore
and a battered herring box
'Scott of Stornoway'

7

'There is evidence that the line of perpetual snow must have descended at that time to a lower level than that attained by our second-class hills, and that almost every Highland valley had its glacier . . . Beds of sea-shells of the boreal type, that belong to those ice ages, may be still found occupying the places in which they had lived and died, many miles inland, and hundreds of feet over the sea-level . . .'

A thin drizzle was drifting over the Black Isle (it seemed a concentration of so much of Scotland) that Sunday when I arrived at Cromarty, making for Hugh Miller's cottage. 'The playing of football on Sunday is strictly forbidden in this park,' by order of Cromarty Town Council. Sounds of hymn singing from a radio somewhere. *Jeannie's But 'n' Ben* was open, selling knick-knacks (Jeannie herself, a grey wiry-haired old crone with a glass eye and a tartan shawl round her shoulders), and further on, a place offering tea and sandwiches: *The Friendly Shop.*

[3] A Maryhill gang song.

Inside the cottage, a woman goes into a disconnected spiel about Miller: 'He cut stones for the graveyard . . . skin disease . . . he was consumptive, he had a hard time as a child . . . second sight . . . he worked in a bank . . . people wrote to him from all over the world, he was a famous geologist . . . involved in church politics, he said that people should be able to elect their own ministers, ye know . . . he killed himself in Edinburgh.'

The upper room has manuscripts and specimens. 'And there it lay, as it had been deposited, far back in the bypast eternity, at the bottom of a muddy sea. But the mud existed now as a dense grey rock.' Ten thousand miles over the fossiliferous deposits of Scotland . . .

a grey smir over the Black Isle
the town dismal
chimneys smoking greasily over the Firth
the Friendly Shop offering tea
happy hymn singing on the radio

fossiliferous deposits

I come away
with the image of a dark figure
hammering reverently at a rock

But I didn't leave Cromarty right away, for there was also Urquhart, who had had great hopes of developing the foresaid town and making it into a hive of commerce and culture before he was attacked by a 'plague of flagitators'. I went up to the Old Kirk, vaguely thinking I might see a gravestone, and I was strolling about in the wilderness of the Old Kirk's graveyard, among the tall weeds and the stones, quiet under the drizzling rain, when I heard a car draw up, and then the gate clanged, and there was this beefy blond-haired Englishman (I heard him) in a kilt (no doubt he had Scottish ancestors), followed by a wee pimpled bespectacled bit of a woman done up in tweed, who barged up to the door of the Kirk as if he owned it, pushed it, banged on it, realised it was closed, and barged off again, with the wee woman scampering behind him. I let the bully boy go, then I left myself.

8

Reading Marpa (another dawn):

When the tiger year was ending
weary of the things of the world
I came to the sanctuary wilderness

the elements of wind and water seethed
the dark hills were clad in white

I don't philosophize but I keep at my task
I sleep little but meditate often

when named I am the man apart

9

'*The islands and promontories along the western seaboard of Scotland*
are noted for their records of intense and prolonged igneous activity
during early Tertiary times. At that period, some 40 million years
ago, volcanic plateaux forming part of a continental region must have
extended continuously along the western coast. By now, owing to
prolonged denudation, vast amounts of the volcanic materials have
disappeared and the broad pipes of former volcanoes are revealed, as
well as still more deeply situated plutonic rocks.'
                                        Official geological survey.

The igneous province. Legends of the rocks. Fragments of the Thule culture.

10

Brief statement (serio-comic) roughly in the style of MacDiarmid:

a rock and river province defying description
(we have of course read all the literature)
but inviting instantaneous perception
à propos red rowan grey heron
lichen grass stone and running water
(see X. Dubrovski on Ecological Syntax)
with as final metaphysical orgasm
the penetration through to the white

which not only defies description
but cannot even faintly be suggested
(as de Gourmont said: suggérer n'est rien*)*
implying a disgust of metaphor
and even of speech itself
a rarity though a reality
bithidh e goirid do mhuir-làn a nisd
whose concreteness is almost an abstraction

from negation to negation, the mind
arrives at this clear space, beyond
opacity, opinions, history, the all-too-human
(cf Coomaraswamy on Nietzsche in The Dance of Shiva*)*
and it is here the aesthetic of almost nothing
comes into action, the merest sign is enough
(see Kuno Meyer: Einführung in die Altirische Dichtung*)*
if prepared by a spaced-out silence

as a thin blaze of quartz in sandstone
nan tàrladh dhuibh a bhith air leirg
has behind it the whole of geology
and in its purity is beyond perfection

II

Jimmy McGinty was here for the weekend—turned up with a
bottle of whisky in one pocket and a bit of shit in the other. He
said Alec Tweedy would have liked to come up as well, but it

was his guru's birthday, and he was away to see him in New York. 'It's his guru's birthday,' says Jimmy, going into one of those convulsive laughs of his. It was a long time since I'd seen Jimmy. Last time I saw him was about seven years ago in London when Joe Torelli was gathering in the boys for his intergalactic tea party ('cosmonauts of inner space'). 'What have you been doin'?' says Jimmy. 'Oh, this and that,' I said, 'coming and going'— I meant 'travelling in the drifting dawn'—and I asked about him. He told me he'd been getting on and off junk. And he had a guru now, too ('I'm supposed no tae drink'), one Klong Rampa, from the land of snows, who had recently settled in Scotland; the same guru as Babe Ruth MacBlake, the American poet, whom he'd just seen in Edinburgh. He asked me if I didn't have a guru. I said, none or many, depending how you looked on it. He looked at me questioningly. I'm a secretive bugger, I said. He went into one of his laughs. For the moment, it's Sgurr Dubh, I said. Who's he, where's he come from? asked Jimmy. He neither comes nor goes—he's a mountain, I said. We got to talking about Buddhism. I suggested all these guru-seekers were just putting Hindu features on to their Christian Father—we had to get further out than that. He claimed I was making too many distinctions (between Buddhism and Christianity, e.g.), and that I was a scholar. That's right, I said, a *wandering* scholar. I like Jimmy. *Namo guru*! And may he plunge, beyond the guru-pond, into the book of a thousand white lights. It turned out, by the way, that Klong, his guru, had quit his monastery, with all those guru-boys flocking to it (bound to stifle any man), and had run away with a wee Scots girl. I said he'd had the right idea. Jimmy went into one of his convulsive laughs. 'A canny get off the women maself,' he said, and told me how the last time he was down in the monastery there was this wee pippin, mmm, with her breasts just about breakin' the sound barrier washing the dishes beside him and he, er, started to chaff her up, ye know, but she turned round to him, as cool as a Tibetan cucumber, and asked did he not remember the guru had said they were to respect complete silence, and that turned him radically off. I said that was probably the wee girl (*oh, mannie, pad me home*) Klong ran away with. Jimmy went into one of his convulsive laughs.

12

Out of the world and into Applecross. To get into Applecross, which is a rocky promontory out off from the rest of the mainland, you have to pass through the beetling Pass of the Cattle which, if it is raining and the mist is thick, can be like going through the gates of a nordic hell (you can take it I've been there). But it's worth it on the other side. You hit a kind of Keltic garden of Eden, less well-known than the islands—even its name suggests that Eden touch (in fact it reads like a synopsis of the whole of Christianity). I was looking for an old friend, a Keltic scholar by the name of Coinnich MacMhaigstir, whom I had known in Glasgow years before. When I finally located the MacMhaigstirs' house, his mother told me he was away, at some congress in Wales, but that I was to come in and have some tea. While she made the tea, I looked out at a couple of fishing smacks at anchor in the rocky little harbour with the thick edge of dark golden weed and the afternoon sunlight, making a late appearance now with the stopping of the rain, glinting on the sea's dark waters.

Mrs MacMhaigstir knew Glasgow well, she had been there several winters with her son. She remembered particularly McLaren's wee bookshop in Argyll Street, which was the place to buy Gaelic Bibles. As for Applecross, she said there were a lot of English moving in, buying up cottages for their summer holidays—'our own boys can't afford them'. She said it would soon be like the Clearances again.

13

MacCrimmon will never come back, never come back, never

come back. That '*Cha till, cha till, cha till MacCruimean*' is what
Donald ban MacCrimmon, the renowned piper, wrote in the
song he composed when he left Skye to take part in the '45. He
said MacLeod might come back, but that the MacCrimmon
never would. The MacLeod did come back, though he'd have
better stayed away, for it's a MacLeod offspring who wrote the
verses ('Skye is My Home'), which are presented in the tourist
shops as 'the ideal souvenir':

> *Sad songs of the islands, bring memories ever so clear*
> *Of pictures as in childhood days, my Island, oh so dear*

But to leave the kitsch, and come back to the pibroch, it ends:

> *Mo chirl tuilleadh riut*
> *Gun dùil tilleadh riut*
> *Gun dùil tilleadh riut*
> *Gun dùil tilleadh riut*
> *Mo chirl tuilleadh riut*
> *Gun dùil tilleadh riut*
> *Mo chirl ri d' chirl na deòir à sileadh*
>
> *(My back to you forever*
> *No hope of your return*
> *No hope of your return*
> *No hope of your return*
> *My back to you forever*
> *No hope of your return*
> *My back to your back and tears flowing)*

—it's a little beauty of a pibroch song, and could be seen as a
lament not only for MacCrimmon but for the whole of Gaelic
culture which his piping represented.

> *Cha till, cha till, cha till MacCruimean*

—sitting here at the window, I'm singing that line over and
over to myself, Keltic *mantra* . . ..

But we probably have to go further back than the Keltic. Back to the Thulean, the pelagian. At least for the ground. But who cares about the ground any more? Everything's up in the air.

14

At Ullapool, I was fed up going about with wet hair, so I bought myself a cap, a sailor's skip-cap, which I happened to set eyes on in an outfitter's window. Later on, I was standing watching the fishing smacks:

> *Quiet waters*
> *Harvest*
> *Kittiwake*
> *Dauntless Star*
> *Catriona*

(and, oops, there's a seal's head sleekly breaking surface) when this English yachtsman asked me which boat I was off. 'The drunken boat,' I said.

15

> *That branch among the fern*
> *was a red stag*
> *sheltering from the rain*

16

To travel north is to travel into the mind. I suppose the same might be said for the south, the east, and the west (any 'pure direction', as it were), but I'm not sure if the north, with maybe the east, isn't privileged. As you go north, the landscape becomes more naked, points of interest become rarer. The self becomes spaced-out. That blue-grey silence among the reeds of the stream—a heron! Wind scouring the sands, and a grey gull struggling to make headway. Little black lochans full of water lilies. Spaced out, and lost in the high open joyance. When you get to the edge, there's next to nothing. Up there, there was a break in the rain, it was at Kyle of Tongue:

a bird yell
emptied my skull

ricks of hay
lined the fields

a fishing smack
lay at quiet anchor—

it was Kyle of Tongue
on a blue morning

17

Here endeth the Book of the Big Rain—interrupted by the arrival at Tigh Geal of Dougie Moffat, the author of the All-Scottish-Arts-Committee prize-winning novel, described in the Scottish reviews as 'authentic', 'down-to-earth', 'pungent', 'real life', 'crying with truth', entitled *Flies in the Porridge*.

THE BOOK OF THE GOLDEN ROOT

*How can people know what we have been
journeying towards?*

Al Hirrâli

I

Let it begin with the young American, member of the Peace
Corps, reading Rimbaud there in the harbour at Marseilles, and
the talk we had about 'wild mystics'. Or better, with the young
girl, lovely to look at, standing at the ship's rail, her blue dress
blowing in the wind.

That evening there'd been a storm, the sky let loose
thunderously over Marseilles, and now the sun had gone down
in a great smothered glow, and that girl there had appeared it
might seem out of the storm itself:

> *what remains in the mind*
> *in the storm-washed emptiness:*
> *a blue dress*
> *blowing in the wind*
> *and the sheer live beauty*
> *of her sixteen year old body*

2

Roundabout reflections in a ten-foot square cabin:

*In the beginning Lieh Tzu was fond of travelling. The adept Hu-ch'iu
Tzu said to him:*
> *'I hear you're fond of travelling. What is it in travelling that pleases you?'*

'*For me,*' *said Lieh Tzu,* '*the pleasure of travelling consists in the appreciation of variety. When most people travel, they merely contemplate what is before their eyes. When I travel, I contemplate the processes of mutability.*'

'*I wonder,*' *said Hu-ch'iu Tzu,* '*whether your travels are not very much the same as other people's, despite the fact that you think them so different. Whenever people look at anything, they are necessarily looking at processes of change, and one may well appreciate the mutability of outside things, while wholly unaware of one's own mutability. Those who take infinite trouble about external travels, have no idea how to set about the sight-seeing that can be done within. The traveller abroad is dependent upon outside things. He whose sight-seeing is inward, can find all he needs in himself. Such is the highest form of travelling, while it is a poor sort of journey that is dependent upon outside things.*'

After this, Lieh Tzu never went anywhere at all, aware that till now he had not really known what travelling means. . .

I suppose I'm still at the stage of 'going places'—yet this going from place to place always leads me, sooner or later, to a no-place. It's the no-place that fundamentally attracts me. Whether or not it is possible to settle there is . . . what remains to be seen.

But even then, even if I really get to the no-place, that won't mean the end of drifting. As the Ch'an master O Hu says: 'Do not say that only those who have not realised the Self are forced to drift about. Even those who have clearly realised it continue to drift.'

They continue to drift, just as they continue to eat rice. Otherwise they would be imprisoning or corpsifying the living truth.

You've got to remain in the current.

3

Tunis. The Arabs used to call it 'Tunis the White', and the

whiteness is still there, if a bit soiled, especially in the old
quarters that are still Arab. They used to call it too 'the sweet-
smelling, flower-bedecked,' and the jasmine-sellers do their best
by hawking their little posies of white flowers to keep it that
way, though car fumes make it a losing battle. Once unequalled
in the Muslim world, maybe Tunis too is destined to become
just another city of illusion.

Anyway, I haven't come here for Tunis. I'll only be in Tunis
a few days, lodging with a friend, a Frenchman, scholar of
Arabic (glasses, goatee, and a ruined stomach), before moving
southwards.

4

There are eight of us, sitting around a big basinful of couscous
in the house of Harouk, who is a customs man at the port of La
Goulette, and there's a good half-dozen bottles of red Mornag
on the table. In the couscous, along with chicken and mutton,
there are partridges, though the shooting season doesn't open
for another three weeks ... 'the ways of Allah'. Harouk talks
through the wine of flush times at La Goulette, and of high
jinks when he was a randy youngster among the Italian girls,
and about later flush times at Marseilles. Then he gets on to his
favourite author, Alexandre Dumas, all of whose novels are
behind him on the bookshelves. Then back to the Thousand
and One Nights of La Goulette. If I told you it all, you could
write a book about it, he says: '*Tu pourrais écrire un bouquin.*' And
it strikes me that I might at that. A picaresque and picturesque
recital of adventures,—yes, The Thousand and One Nights of
La Goulette. I'd turn Harouk the *hâbleur* and *bon vivant*, in reality
a bit of a bore, into a culture-hero, a Gargantua, a Don Juan
and a Haroun al Raschid all in one. What he's saying now, '*tu
pourrais écrire un bouquin*', is exactly what an old acquaintance
of mine, up in the Gorbals of Glasgow, told me one night he'd
invited me over to *The Rising Sun* for a 'refreshment': 'All

y'need's a tape-recorder, boy, and it'll put y'right on top'. Right on top of what, I asked him. But up there in Glasgow I did actually start in on a book of this kind, or at least started noting down incidents and anecdotes around a character called Mungo Reilly, a kind of incarnation of the spirit of Glasgow. But it got lost along the way. Now, however, the idea's fleetingly back, with Harouk here and the port of Tunis, and the red Mornag. Maybe some day. Some day in the evening. But no. The time for such books is past, I tell myself. It's now a new drifting dawn, and there are other, more radical, things to be done. Yes, no drama, no romance, but the truth of the drifting—the free mind's arabesque.

5

There's a little library, belonging to the Pères Blancs, in the old quarters of Tunis, impasse Kradechji, and I spend a good part of my afternoons in there, with Tunisian students around me working on Middle Eastern politics, the economic situation of the Maghreb and other themes of the kind—university students preparing theses, working at national problems, self-consciously modernist, while this drifter is sitting in there among them, nation-less, and not only not moving with the times, not even moving against them: working in sheer idiosyncrasy (but beyond that, the cool universal stream). He's not reading Bourguiba, but the tenth century Abu Bakr al-Kalâbâdhi: 'If the ecstasy of a man is weak, he will be all out to make a show of it. But if it is real and strong, he will be silent.' And Hâfim al-Asamur: 'Every morning, Satan says to me: What will you eat, and what will you wear, and where will you dwell?' Or again: 'On the hat of poverty are inscribed three renunciations—quit this world, quit the next world, quit quitting.'

Wandering with the Arabic scholar through the streets; learning a few phrases of the language; reading in the library—then, after five days or so, on the road.

6

I'm back in biblical country. I'm moving with my feet through
the pages of a book, and it's the illustrated Bible I possessed as
a child (in fact there was more than one of them, in the country
I was born in, you can end up with a whole library of Old and
New Testaments before you reach puberty).

That old shepherd, and his flock of sheep and goats spreading
slowly over the sunburned landscape . . . That young veiled girl
passing:

*'Thine eyes are like the fish pools of Heshbon, by the gate of Bath-
Rabbim.'*

The feeling that I'm starting from the beginning again.

7

There's a race of French schoolteachers, called *'co-opérants'*, lent
by the French government to Tunisia for varying periods,
bearers too often of a semi-colonialist mentality, earning fat
salaries (about twice what they would earn in France, and at
least three times what the normal Tunisian teacher can make),
that infest the country north, south, east and west. It was my
misfortune to hitch-hike with a couple of them on the road from
Tunis to Nabeul.

One was a teacher of philosophy, who'd already spent a
couple of years in the country and, as he never tired of saying,
'knew the ropes', and 'everybody worth knowing'. He was
acting as guide and chaperone to the other twerp, a teacher of
French and Latin, who'd just arrived, and was full of
illuminating questions such as:

'Is that a lycée, Hervé?'

to which Hervé would reply authoritatively:

'Yes,'

or

'How much can you get me a meergoum for, Hervé?', to which, after due reflection, Hervé would reply, equally authoritatively:

'Fifty dinars.'

In fact, the conversation between these two shits was all about hotels, their lay-out, the food in them (*'Excellent'*), the price of the rooms (*'C'est correct'*), and about their salaries, exactly how much they'd have at their disposal, and how much they would be able to bank in France. As the philosophy teacher put it:

'Avec du fric, tu peux tout faire.'

Tunisia being 'culturally under-developed' too (the people here having 'no notion of rationality': 'simple intuitives', 'subjective'), they wouldn't even have to work hard at all, just put in a few easy hours, draw their salary, and enjoy the luxury of their villa at Sidi Bou.

I was glad to see the last of these two when they dropped me in Nabeul, making for their rooms in a 'palace' at Hammamet.

8

That night, I saw a yellow flame dancing. But it was nothing so insubstantial as a flame, it was the solid body of an Arab girl doing a belly dance, prophesying fleshly delights with breasts, hips, belly and thighs, *ghoonjing* (arab: *ghoonj wa taghneej*—the art of moving in coition) for all she was worth. And next day the sun did a belly dance all day in the sky.

Life, brothers, is a belly dance!

9

'The wine-seller
pouring the golden wine
and me drinking
beside us a girl
with perfect breasts
dancing'

10

'M'sieu, M'sieu, donne-moi l'argent.'
   It's Youssef puts forward the request, but he is not alone, around me with him are Ahmed, Habib, Abd-el-Karim, Moncef and Brahim, kids who have seen me walking here through the medina of Monastir, and have latched on to me. They all know too, or at least the sharp-eyed Youssef knows, that I have a packet of biscuits in my rucksack, for he saw me buying them at the little grocery. But he hasn't got round to the biscuits yet, he starts off with the usual: *'donne-moi l'argent'*. I say I don't have any to give away, just to set the ball rolling, for if I gave him a coin right away there'd be no game, and no fun. We walk together through the streets of Monastir, and I learn their names, and they ask me where I come from and where I'm going ... At length, with a smile and a nod at the rucksack, Youssef says: *'M'sieu, donne-moi l'argent, et j'achèterai biscuits comme toi'*. I continue the game for a while, then we all squat down at a corner and I share out the biscuits among us.

11

In Kairouan, the wool merchant (multi-coloured hanks of wool all around) offers a glass of tea from his little blue enamel pot set on the charcoal-burner. His son then suggests a tour of the carpet-weaving families in the street. In one, working at a loom with her mother—hanging at the top of the loom are a hand of Fatma in metal, a shell, and a smaller Fatma hand cut out of cloth—there is a lovely young girl about fifteen years old. She's sitting like a tailor before the loom, her skirt up over her thighs, and while I'm leaning over supposedly to admire the pattern of the carpet, it's those lovely thighs I'm looking at, and I'm not sure she doesn't know it, for when I get on my way again, she gives me a smile that melts the marrow in my bones, and leaves me, out in the sunlit street, full of a desire that the Grand Mosque can't satisfy, can't satisfy at all.

12

'I will take her to the desert and speak to her heart.'

13

I'd picked some Barbary figs, for a midday meal, and my hands were covered with the prickles. Just outside Msaken, I'd got a lift with a French couple, and now at El Djem, where they'd come to admire the colosseum, the woman had taken a pair of tweezers from her toilet bag, and was extracting the prickles as we stood beside their car. Pretty soon, there are a dozen men of El Djem around us, all wanting to have a go with the tweezers, and one hurries back into his shop and comes out—with a pair of pliers, intending to have a go with *them*. When my hands have won the attentions of five El Djemians, all expert prickle-extracters (the man with the squint wields the tweezers with great confidence and delight, closing them all the time, except maybe for the odd chance, on sheer vacuity), I'm advised to finish off the process by rubbing my hands in sand—there's a pile close by, where two or three men show me the best way of going about it, each according to his idea. Then the woman recovers her tweezers and, with numerous farewells, we get on the road again.

14

'*I have extracted by means of the pincers of self-knowledge the thorns of divers opinions from the deep recesses of my mind.*'

15

At night, in the old quarter of Sfax, after wandering among the little workshops of the tailors, the cobblers, the smiths, the jewellers, etc. (and when I say little workshops, I mean *little* workshops—the Arab can live and work on the space of a mat; though it may be this same Arab, or his brother, you see out in the vastness of the countryside, miles of desertic landscape all around him, on foot, a single point in the emptiness), I go into the mosque, evening prayers are on, and, sandals in hand, find myself a spot away in a corner, in semi-obscurity, a spot which is visited later only by a wandering cat. And I sit there, with the murmur of prayer from the large hall, doing a little concentration on my own—religionless, prayerless, but concentrated:

'The truth flashes by like lightning in between the gaps created by the absence of thought.'

I'm the last to leave the mosque.

16

'*There is nothing inside this coat but Allah!*'

17

Near Gabès:

> *The old black man*
> *in tattered shirt and faded blue shorts*
> *walks up and down the beach*

up and down the beach
slowly
all morning
on the lookout—
then suddenly he crouches
eyes fixed
and stalks into the sea
his net at the ready
casts it
and carefully
hauls it in:

ten silver fish
flapping in its meshes

18

Eating a pomegranate in the palm grove at Gabès.

19

Out of Gabès, moving west. Wind blowing. Little sand columns whirling and whisking out in the scrubland. A herd of black goats. Long line of telegraph poles leading into nothingness. My dusty feet. A woman goes by, water jar on her back, dark red robes, heavy silver jewelry. Sidi Mannsour. Then the scrubland again. Tents stretched over walls of earth and brushwood. El Guetar. Soon after, the palm trees begin, and it's the oasis of Gafsa.

20

In the Oued Gabès I touched the breasts of the wind.

21

There's a high-walled pool in Gafsa, dating from Roman times, and there's always a crowd of kids there, ready to dive from the wall for a coin, or, still higher, from one of the two palm trees that grow above. A little brown-skinned girl, about eight years old, dressed in a pair of tattered knickers, henna-red hair and hands, smoking a cigarette, offers to do a dive, '*tête d'abord*', and just as she says it, a friend of hers, the exact replica of herself, turns up, hair dripping wet, having already done the dive, and now saying: '*donne-moi l'argent*'. They hang on to me, laughing, lascivious little creatures, and they must have been getting too excited, for an older boy comes up and shoos them away. He asks '*où allez-vous, M'sieu?*', and I say I'm going to Foum Tataouine, which is as much as to say: the end of the world. He wishes me a good journey and moves off. A band of boys, from ten to twelve years old, have been waiting for their chance. Up they come now:

'*Hé, M'sieu, toi faire l'amour avec Bédouine dans l'oasis? Deux cents millimes . . ..*'

22

I'd wanted to move on further down to Tozeur and Nefta and the Chott El Djerid, but heavy rains had fallen in Algeria, and the oueds were flooded, and the car I'd come in with decided it was dangerous to go further and was making back to Gabès, so I went with it. Back to Gabès, and then from Gabès to Medenine. And from Medenine all the way down to Foum Tataouine, and the berber country around it.

23

When Morienus the Alchemist was asked by the Prince Kallid (seventh century) why he preferred to wander in mountains and deserts rather than live in a monastery, he answered: 'I do not doubt that in monasteries and brotherhoods I would find greater repose, whereas it is tiring work in the mountains and deserts, but . . . the gateway to peace is narrow, and no one can enter it without some suffering.'

24

Guermessa is built on three hills, the houses inserted in them, distinguished by a flash of whitewash round the doors. Halfway up the middle hill, a dark red *malhafa*, spread to dry on a wall, attracts and holds the eye.

The three hills are called Margab Essallah, Matmana, and Aigri. I climb up the central hill, Matmana, with two young boys who've offered themselves as guides. On rocks on the hill top, footprints marked in paint or carved, with names and dates, sometimes the outline of a fish as good-luck sign. The boys tell me that the men of the village climb up here on the seventh day of their marriage and make these marks.

An *instituteur* from Tataouine—'*Moi, j'enseigne le langage arabe et français*'—met up there on Matmana says that 'the people are hard here, but they have white souls' ('*Les gens sont durs ici, mais ils ont l'âme blanche*').

Rocky, desertic landscape. Down in the village, a gathering of red-robed women—it's a marriage, the boys say. And then a chanting rises in the clear air, a chanting interspersed with calls: red cries in the clear air.

Down off Matmana, we go to the village café, a hole in the rock, with a couple of shelves bearing packets of biscuits, coffee, and tins of sardines. The little pot is set on the *kanoun*. A *33 tours* is set on the record-player. And the six of us huddled there in the hole in the rock have a little festival.

25

'I would have you strip away every impediment of your body, scour your heart till it is free of passion, and travel through the desolate wilds. For to the south there is a place called the Land of Power. Its people are ignorant and unspoiled, negligent of their interests, and of few desires. They know how to make, but do not know how to hoard. They give, but seek no return. They live and move thoughtlessly and at random, yet every step they take tallies with the Great Plan. They know how to enjoy life while it lasts, and are ready to be put away when death comes.'

26

Lines for a Berber brooch:

> Crude silver
> crescent-shaped
> berber moon
>
> figure of the fish
> and the bird
> and the flower
>
> heavy in the hand
> gleam of last light

27

A circle of sphinx-like hills, and in the centre a rocky pile. On this rocky pile, Chenini, the dwellings worked into it: cut into the rock, or made with its stone. Many ruins, but livable places still among the ruins, and one or two houses even have the firm appearance of little forts.

Middle of the afternoon. Hard white sunlight. The men are gathered in the shade of the mosque. Asses and camels in the courtyards. Figs and dates drying on the roofs. Women in dark red going about their tasks.

I follow the track up to the top of the hill.

Up there, suddenly, the crying of a hundred cocks, all the cocks of Chenini crowing in the mid-afternoon. There's knowledge and ignorance, desperation and joy in it.

28

'Ah, marvellous obscurity
Seed of my whiteness'

29

There were three of them round that table in the café at Medenine, drinking beer and eating beans—a pile of brown bean-shells growing steadily under the table. I'd come in for a cool, quiet drink myself, and was making for the door when one of them got up and came over to me, asking if I was French. I said yes. He told me he was taking a correspondence course in French, and had a problem in grammar which I would be able to solve for him. When we'd got the grammar straightened out, he invited me to their table. They were teachers of Arab literature.

They asked me what I was doing in Tunisia, and I said I was just travelling around. And they asked me what I'd liked best of all I'd seen, and I talked about the girl dancing, and the smile of the girl in Kairouan, and the man moving across the scrubland and the wind blowing, and the crying of the cocks on Chenini. Then one asked me out of the blue what were the finest lines about love in modern poetry, and I said the first lines that came into my head, and they weren't modern, and were they even about love:

There is nothing here but this cave in the field's midst
A wild place, unlit and unfilled

30

On the market at Mount Souk, I meet the Professor of Sheep, alias Semi-colon. That requires perhaps a little explanation.

Semi-colon, who sells everything from sheepskins to dried scorpions ('If these damned creatures don't find anything to kill, on Fridays they kill themselves,') introduced himself as a Professor of Sheep ('*professeur de brebis*') to a French tourist who'd said he was a '*professeur*'. And he elaborated: 'I am Professor Ali Habib, professor of sheep, famous in the entire universe. I'm the big chief. When I say to my sheep, go, they go, and when I say, come, they come. I have four houses, and four wives—one German, one French, one American, and one Tunisian. I am looking for a fifth. She must weigh two hundred kilos. But the women never stay long. Only five or six days at a stretch. They are happy and contented till they see me take my *neffa*, then they skedaddle.' At this, he gives a demonstration of how he takes his *neffa* (snuff), producing a little tin box from his pocket, pinching in his forefinger and thumb, then sticking his thumb into the right hand corner of his mouth, between gum and lip, then running it along to the left. 'You see,' he says, reperforming the gesture, 'that's why I'm also known as Semi-colon.'

31

'With a little earth, one makes many forms,' says the potter at Guellala.

32

'*L'essence pure, sans alcool,*' explains the perfume-merchant, dressed in a spotless jebba, bringing out his 'secret of the desert', which he says is made from a blue flower growing in the wastes. And he tells me his life-story: '*C'est le mekhtoub.*' All he has left now, pure essences.

33

There's a Ghost Room in Jerba, a room in an old mosque, now converted into a museum. The idea was that if you spent a night in this room, reciting the Koran, at dawn a girl would appear to you, and would lead you down to 'the underground people.' There, underground, the conditions of union with this woman would be settled.

I didn't spend a night in the mosque, I didn't recite the Koran, but I've met that girl.

34

'Since we took leave of you, we have gone down to a sea, and the shore of that sea is our abode.

And above this abode of ours there is a sun. The setting of this sun is within us, and its rising is also within us.

What is this sun? What is its meaning and its secret?

We have gone down to a sea whose name is emptiness . . .'